Administrator's Guide
Interpreting the Common Core State Standards to Improve Mathematics Education

Matthew R. Larson
Lincoln Public Schools
Lincoln, Nebraska

www.nctm.org/more4u
Access code: AGI14288

NCTM
NATIONAL COUNCIL OF
TEACHERS OF MATHEMATICS

Copyright © 2011 by
The National Council of Teachers of Mathematics, Inc.
1906 Association Drive, Reston, VA 20191-1502
(703) 620-9840; (800) 235-7566; www.nctm.org
All rights reserved

Library of Congress Cataloging-in-Publication Data

Larson, Matthew R.
  Administrator's guide : interpreting the common core state standards to improve mathematics
education / Matthew R. Larson.
    p. cm.
  Includes bibliographical references.
  ISBN 978-0-87353-695-0
  1. Mathematics--Study and teaching--United States. 2. School management and organization--
United States. I. National Council of Teachers of Mathematics. II. Title. III. Title: Interpreting the
common core state standards to improve mathematics education.
  QA13.L355 2011
  510.71'073--dc23
                                    2011034855

The National Council of Teachers of Mathematics is a public voice of mathematics education, supporting
teachers to ensure equitable mathematics learning of the highest quality for all students through vision,
leadership, professional development, and research.

Printed in the United States of America

Contents

Preface vii

Acknowledgments ix

Introduction 1

How U.S. Students Are Performing in Mathematics 3

    Performance of U.S. Students over Time 3

    Performance of U.S. Students vs. Their International Peers 4

Why Common Core State Standards for Mathematics? 7

A Shared Vision 8

Interpreting the Common Core State Standards 10

    Prekindergarten–Grade 8 10

    Grades 9–12 11

Emphasizing Mathematical Practices and Processes 14

    CCSSM's View of Mathematical Practices 14

    NCTM's Longstanding Emphasis on Process 15

    A Comparison of the CCSSM and NCTM Approaches to Process 16

The Six NCTM Principles: The Foundation of a High-Quality Mathematics Program 19

    Achieving Equity 20

    Focusing the Curriculum and Making It Coherent 21

    Ensuring High-Quality Teaching 22

    Enriching Learning 25

    Assessing Appropriately 26

    Teaching with Technology 28

Contents

Examples of High-Quality Mathematics Classrooms...29

    Elementary School Classroom Example...29

    Middle School Classroom Example 30

    High School Classroom Example 32

    Elements of High-Quality Classrooms 34

        What are students doing? 34

        What is the teacher doing? 35

Putting the NCTM Principles into Action in Your School 37

    How Administrators Can Support the Principles 37

    Observing and Evaluating a Mathematics Classroom 39

    Developing and Supporting Professional Development 41

        Goals of mathematics professional development 41

        Features that support professional development goals 43

    Supporting New Teachers 44

Why Family Involvement Is Important 46

    What Information and Resources Should Be Communicated to Families? 46

    Ways to Communicate with Families 47

Conclusion 48

Frequently Asked Questions 49

    Are the traditional basics still important? 49

    How should students be grouped? 49

    What is the role of practice, drill, and homework in mathematics instruction? 50

    What are the appropriate uses of manipulatives in the mathematics classroom? 51

    Will calculators and other technology hurt students' computational skills? 51

    Should elementary schools use mathematics specialists? 51

Contents

Should schools invest in mathematics instructional coaches? 52

Where can research be found to support effective mathematics instruction? 52

How can ELL students be supported in learning mathematics? 53

What are effective strategies for teaching students with difficulties in mathematics? 54

What should be used for mathematics intervention, or RtI? 55

What are effective strategies to motivate students to learn mathematics? 56

Additional Resources **57**

CCSSM Resources 57

Leadership Resources 57

High School Reasoning and Sense Making Resources 58

Curriculum Resources 58

Diversity, Intervention, and Differentiation Resources 59

Professional Development Resources 59

Mathematical Discourse Resources 59

Early Childhood Resources 60

Appendix A: Interpretation Charts **61**

Interpretation Charts for Prekindergarten–Grade 8 61

Sample Interpretation Chart for High School 87

Appendix B: Mathematical Practices and Processes Chart **92**

References **99**

Preface

Nearly a decade ago, the National Council of Teachers of Mathematics (NCTM) published *Administrator's Guide: How to Support and Improve Mathematics Education in Your School* (Mirra 2003). In the years since that publication, the educational landscape across the United States in general, and in mathematics education in particular, has dramatically changed. For example, in 2003 the landmark federal legislation No Child Left Behind (NCLB 2002) was barely one year old, and the consequences of the law were not well understood. Today, hundreds of school districts all across the country are facing increasing penalties for failing to meet Adequate Yearly Progress targets; administrators and teachers are under increasing pressure to produce results or face possible termination; schools are being closed or reconstituted; and pressure to change teacher evaluation systems, tenure, and collective bargaining is mounting.

In 2003, no one could imagine the formation of a national math panel. Today, not only has a such a panel—the National Mathematics Advisory Panel (NMAP)—been convened and a report issued (NMAP 2008), but as of this writing, forty-four states and the District of Columbia have adopted voluntary national standards in mathematics, known as the Common Core State Standards for Mathematics (CCSSM), produced by the Common Core State Standards Initiative (CCSSI 2010). In addition, two national assessment consortia—Partnership for the Assessment of Readiness for College and Careers (PARCC) and Smarter Balanced Assessment Consortium (SBAC)—are creating new assessment systems for determining student attainment of the Common Core State Standards for Mathematics. Both assessment systems are currently scheduled for implementation in the 2014–2015 school year.

The last decade has clearly been one of unprecedented and rapid change in mathematics education. Published reports and major documents that have significantly influenced mathematics education since 2003 include the following:

> *How Students Learn: Mathematics in the Classroom* (National Research Council [NRC] 2005)
>
> *Curriculum Focal Points for Prekindergarten through Grade 8 Mathematics: A Quest for Coherence* (NCTM 2006)
>
> *Mathematics Teaching Today: Improving Practice, Improving Student Learning* (NCTM 2007)
>
> *Rising Above the Gathering Storm* (Committee on Science, Engineering, and Public Policy [CSEPP] 2007)
>
> *Foundations for Success: The National Mathematics Advisory Panel Final Report* (NMAP 2008)
>
> *Focus in High School Mathematics: Reasoning and Sense Making* (NCTM 2009)

Mathematics Learning in Early Childhood: Paths toward Excellence and Equity (NRC 2009)

Common Core State Standards for Mathematics (CCSSI 2010)

The purpose of this updated *Administrator's Guide* is to help school and district leaders make sense of the many recommendations that have been made over the past decade, with a special emphasis on the Common Core State Standards for Mathematics and the similarities between these new standards and those outlined in NCTM's influential *Principles and Standards for School Mathematics* (NCTM 2000). In addition, this guide draws on a number of recent NCTM publications and other NCTM documents, including Position Statements and Research Briefs, and summarizes and organizes many of the recommendations found in these diverse publications in this one guide for the convenience of school administrators and other mathematics education leaders.

Although this publication is titled *Administrator's Guide: Interpreting the Common Core State Standards to Improve Mathematics Education,* anyone who has an interest in improving mathematics teaching and learning can gain something of value from it. Research increasingly indicates that many individuals within a school can and do contribute to the work of leading and managing the school. Influential leadership within schools—that is, the cadre of individuals to whom teachers look for mathematics education guidance and advice on curricular, assessment, and instructional issues—is often widely distributed across a school and not limited to the positional leader (Spillane 2011). Teachers may look to instructional math coaches, colleagues in their professional learning community, mathematics specialists, department chairs, or knowledgeable others to provide them with information on how to improve mathematics teaching and learning. This guide can support anyone who finds himself or herself in the position of working to improve mathematics education—either alone or in the role of supporting others.

Although much has changed in the last decade, one thing has been constant: the National Council of Teachers of Mathematics has remained a global leader and authority in mathematics education. NCTM has steadfastly advocated for changes in school mathematics programs to ensure that all students have access to the highest-quality mathematics teaching and learning, preparing them for success in school today and for college or careers tomorrow in a world of work that can only be imagined. This guide provides a starting place for you, as an administrator or other mathematics education leader, to acquire the knowledge that you need about mathematics education, the Common Core State Standards for Mathematics, and ways in which you can support and improve mathematics education in your school and district.

This guide begins by examining the importance of school mathematics for college and career readiness. It then briefly surveys the current state of mathematics achievement within the United States as well as how students in the United States compare with their peers internationally. An explanation of the Common Core State Standards for Mathematics follows, with an emphasis on CCSSM's Standards for Mathematical Practice and their connection to NCTM's Process Standards, as articulated in *Principles and Standards for School Mathematics* (NCTM 2000).

The guide examines the NCTM Principles for a high-quality mathematics program and then provides brief vignettes from elementary, middle, and high school classrooms to give the reader snapshots of high-quality mathematics instruction. From there, the guide moves on to specific actions that school leaders can take to support and improve mathematics education in their school or district. The section "Frequently Asked Questions" offers guidance on questions that often come up in mathematics education.

The guide concludes by presenting a list of additional resources that can support you and teachers as you work together to improve mathematics education within your school or district. Two appendixes supply detailed information about the connections between CCSSM and NCTM's Standards for school mathematics and supporting publications.

Throughout, the guide cites relevant and current research so that you can have confidence in the recommendations that it offers and will be able to defend your own policy and program recommendations to critics. In time, by using this guide and the additional resources that NCTM provides, you can successfully implement CCSSM and make a significant difference in the quality of teaching and learning of mathematics in your school or district.

Go to http://www.nctm.org/more4u and enter the access code printed on this book's title page for a version of Appendix A with live links for NCTM resources.

Acknowledgments

In many ways, this guide is a combination of two previous NCTM publications. It updates NCTM's *Administrator's Guide: How to Support and Improve Mathematics Education in Your School* (Mirra 2003), in part by incorporating portions of NCTM's *Making It Happen: A Guide to Interpreting and Implementing Common Core State Standards for Mathematics* (NCTM 2010). Some of the material from both of these publications is used here exactly as it originally appeared in them. Readers are encouraged to use *Making It Happen* and its accompanying online database as a tool to support implementation of the Common Core State Standards for Mathematics. Sincere thanks are extended to those who prepared both of these previous NCTM publications.

Introduction

Today's world is very different from the world of even a few years ago. We are all bombarded with data that we must absorb, sort, organize, and use to make increasingly complex and critical decisions. The underpinnings of everyday life and participation in our democratic society, such as making purchasing decisions, choosing insurance or health plans, planning retirement, and understanding the complex issues surrounding the national debt, require mathematical competence. Business and industry increasingly seek employees who can collaboratively solve complex real-life problems for which the solution paths are unclear, explain and justify their thinking to others, identify and analyze trends in data, and effectively use modern technology.

Taking advanced mathematics is increasingly linked to college, career, and economic success. Recent data indicate that more students must continue their education after high school and pursue paths in mathematical and technical occupations to find economic success. For example, growth in math-intensive science and engineering jobs is expected to outpace overall job growth by three to one (National Science Board 2008). Taking advanced math in high school is one of the best predictors of college completion, increasing the college completion rate from 36 to 59 percent among low-income students (Adelman 2006). Among students whose parents did not graduate from college, taking advanced math courses more than doubles their own chances of attending college (Choy 2002; Horn and Nuñez 2000).

Partly as a result of the correlation between advanced mathematics course enrollment and college completion rates, twenty states and the District of Columbia have established high school graduation requirements that include mathematics through at least what is typically taught in an algebra 2 course (Achieve 2011). Although some critics point out that not all students need to attend a four-year college, the reality is that students today who terminate their education with a high school diploma face a bleak future. The Bureau of Labor Statistics estimates that 80 percent of the fastest-growing job categories will require some form of postsecondary education or training (Achieve 2005). Achieve (2003) has argued that the skills that high school graduates need to be successful in college are the same as those needed in the job market for jobs that pay enough to support a family, provide benefits, and offer a pathway for career advancement. Some studies have found that the math skills required of electricians, construction workers, and plumbers, for example, match the preparation necessary to do well in college (ACT 2006).

Taking advanced mathematics has a direct impact on students' future earnings. Research indicates that taking advanced mathematics courses accounts for up to one-quarter of the income gap between students from low- and middle-class families ten years after high school completion (Rose and Betts 2004). Over the last half-century, the nature of the U.S. economy has dramatically changed. In 1950, 60 percent of jobs in the country required no particular skills beyond high school; in 2005, only 14 percent of jobs were classified in the same way (Achieve 2005). The economy can simply no longer absorb unskilled workers at middle-class wages, and this reality threatens our societal infrastructure over the long term unless we give all students the skills that they need to compete in a knowledge-based world (Darling-Hammond 2006). Students who are not prepared to continue their education after high school will increasingly find themselves part of a growing underclass whose members find it more and more difficult to engage productively in society (Darling-Hammond 2007). We have an obligation to our students, and to the future of our society, to ensure that all students have access to the highest-quality mathematics teaching and learning so that they are prepared to continue learning beyond high school and become fully functioning members of society.

How U.S. Students Are Performing in Mathematics

National and international studies of students' achievement in mathematics in the United States are both discouraging and hopeful. Overall, students in the United States at all grade levels are not performing well enough in mathematics. In addition, achievement gaps based on ethnicity and socioeconomic status have in some cases narrowed slightly, but they have remained relatively static and significant over the past twenty years.

Performance of U.S. Students over Time

The National Assessment of Educational Progress (NAEP) is administered in math in grades 4, 8, and 12 and ranks students' performance according to four levels of achievement—below basic, basic, proficient, and advanced. The NAEP showed the following major results for students in grades 4 and 8 in 2009 (NCES 2009):

- Gains in fourth-grade average scores seen in earlier years did not continue from 2007 to 2009, but fourth-grade scores were nevertheless higher than the scores in the six assessment years from 1990 to 2005.

- Gains in eighth-grade average scores seen in earlier years did continue at grade 8 between 2007 and 2009. Eighth-grade scores in 2009 were higher than the scores in the seven assessment years from 1990 to 2007.

- The percentage of fourth graders performing at or above proficient (39%) in 2009 was unchanged from 2007 but remained higher than in the assessment years from 1990 to 2005.

- The percentage of eighth graders performing at or above proficient (34%) in 2009 was higher than in 2007 and in all earlier assessment years.

- At grade 4, there were no significant changes in the average mathematics scores from 2007 to 2009 for students in different ethnic groups, but scores for all groups were higher than in 1990.

- At grade 8, the score gap between white and black students in 2009 was not significantly different from the gap in 2007 but was narrower than in 1990.

- At grade 8, the gap between white and Latino students in 2009 was not significantly different from the gaps in either 2007 or 1990.

- At grade 8, average mathematics scores were higher in 2009 than in both 2007 and 1990 for most ethnic groups.

- Significant score gaps persisted between white students and their black and Latino peers in 2009. All three groups had made significant progress, but the gaps were not significantly different from the gaps in 2007 or 1990.

The National Assessment of Educational Progress also conducts an assessment of long-term trends. This assessment was most recently given in the 2007–2008 school year to students at ages 9, 13, and 17. The long-term trend assessments make it possible to chart educational progress in the nation since the early 1970s. The latest long-term trend assessment showed the following major results (Rampey, Dion, and Donahue 2009):

- Average scores for 9- and 13-year-olds increased since 2004, while the average score for 17-year-olds did not change significantly.

- Average scores for 9- and 13-year-olds were higher in 2008 than in 1973.

- The average score for 17-year-olds in 2008 was not significantly different from that in 1973.

- Across all three age groups, neither the white-black nor white-Latino gap in mathematics changed significantly from 2004 to 2008, but both were smaller in 2008 than in 1973.

Performance of U.S. Students vs. Their International Peers

The Trends in International Mathematics and Science Study (TIMSS) 2007 marked the fourth time since 1995 that this international comparison of student achievement was conducted. Major findings of this study included the following (Gonzales et al. 2008):

- In 2007, the average mathematics scores of both U.S. fourth graders and eighth graders were higher than the TIMSS scale average.

- The average U.S. fourth-grade mathematics score was higher than those of students in 23 of 35 other countries, lower than those of students in 8 countries (all located in Asia or Europe), and not measurably different from those of students in the remaining 4 countries.

- The average U.S. eighth-grade mathematics score was higher than those of students in 37 of 47 other countries, lower than those of students in 5 countries (all located in Asia), and not measurably different from those in the other 5 countries.

- The average mathematics scores for both U.S. fourth- and eighth-grade students were higher in 1995 than in 2007.

- In 2007, 10 percent of U.S. fourth graders and 6 percent of U.S. eighth-graders scored at or above the advanced international benchmark in mathematics.

Another achievement concern is the strong correlation between socioeconomic status and mathematics achievement in the United States. Analysis of TIMSS data indicates that among participating countries, the United States has one of the strongest correlations between socioeconomic status and mathematics achievement (Schmidt et al. 2011).

The Programme for International Student Assessment (PISA) provides another look at the performance of U.S. students in an international context. PISA focuses on students near the end of their compulsory education and emphasizes the application of knowledge and skills necessary for full participation in society. PISA was most recently administered in 2009. The table on the next page shows where the top 50 participating countries rank in mathematics performance (OECD 2010).

In summary, the mathematics performance of U.S. students in elementary and middle school, as measured by NAEP, has improved modestly over the last four decades, and although achievement gaps have in some cases narrowed over the same time period, significant achievement gaps remain. Internationally, U.S. students' performance lags behind that of students in many countries that are our economic peers. These persistent lags in the performance of U.S. students in mathematics, both nationally and internationally, contributed to the push for the Common Core State Standards for Mathematics.

2009 PISA Mathematics Rankings

Country	Mean Score	Country	Mean Score
Shanghai–China	600	Sweden	494
Singapore	562	Czech Republic	493
Hong Kong–China	555	United Kingdom	492
Korea	546	Hungary	490
Chinese Taipei	543	Luxembourg	489
Finland	541	**United States**	**487**
Liechtenstein	536	Ireland	487
Switzerland	534	Portugal	487
Japan	529	Spain	483
Canada	527	Italy	483
Netherlands	526	Latvia	482
Macao–China	525	Lithuania	477
New Zealand	519	Russian Federation	468
Belgium	515	Greece	466
Australia	514	Croatia	460
Germany	513	Dubai (UAF)	453
Estonia	512	Israel	447
Iceland	507	Turkey	445
Denmark	503	Serbia	442
Slovenia	501	Azerbaijan	431
Norway	498	Bulgaria	428
France	497	Romania	427
Slovak Republic	497	Uruguay	427
Austria	496	Chile	421
Poland	495	Thailand	419

Why Common Core State Standards for Mathematics?

The Common Core State Standards Initiative was a state-led process spearheaded by the Council of Chief State School Officers (CCSSO) and the National Governors Association Center for Best Practices (NGA Center). The goal was to create a set of career- and college-readiness standards in mathematics (and English/language arts) to ensure that all students graduate from high school ready for college or work. A set of K–8 standards outlines a grade-by-grade road map to prepare students for the career- and college-readiness standards at the high school level.

Two primary concerns motivated the Common Core State Standards Initiative. First, inconsistent curricular standards, assessments, and proficiency cut scores across the fifty states raised equity issues (Reed 2009). These different systems often led to wide disparities between student scores on state assessments in reading and math and student performance on the National Assessment of Educational Progress (Schneider 2007).

Second, as previously discussed, concern that U.S. students are not leaving school with the skills necessary for success in college or the workforce is widespread and increasing. Results of international assessments, including PISA (Baldi et al. 2007) and TIMSS (Gonzales et al. 2008) indicate that U.S. students do not achieve at the level of students in other advanced countries in mathematics, raising concern about U.S. economic competitiveness in an environment where U.S. students compete with students all across the globe.

A Shared Vision

The Common Core State Standards for Mathematics (CCSSM) build on many years of work by NCTM to define the mathematics that students need to know and be able to do. NCTM became the first national organization to develop content standards in mathematics with its publication of *Curriculum and Evaluation Standards for School Mathematics* (1989), which was subsequently revised and updated as *Principles and Standards for School Mathematics* (2000). More recently, the Council published *Curriculum Focal Points for Prekindergarten through Grade 8 Mathematics: A Quest for Coherence* (2006) to address issues of curricular consistency, coherence, and depth in the school years before high school. In 2009, NCTM published *Focus in High School Mathematics: Reasoning and Sense Making* to articulate a vision for high school mathematics based on reasoning and sense making and encouraging students to develop reasoning habits throughout their mathematics learning. Since 2009, NCTM has published four additional books in the Focus in High School Mathematics series on specific topics (see the section "Additional Resources" in this guide).

While CCSSM was in development, NCTM organized review panels to provide extensive comments and detailed suggestions to the developers and writers on every successive draft after the first. NCTM diligently monitored the development of CCSSM and advised CCSSI throughout the process. In June of 2010, NCTM expressed its support for the goal and intent of the Common Core State Standards for Mathematics. In the summer of 2011, NCTM helped found the Mathematics Common Core Coalition (MC³), consisting of the National Council of Teachers of Mathematics, the National Council of Supervisors of Mathematics (NCSM), the Association of Mathematics Teacher Educators (AMTE), the Association of State Supervisors of Mathematics (ASSM), the Council of Chief State School Officers (CCSSO), the National Governors Association (NGA), the Smarter Balanced Assessment Consortium (SBAC), and the Partnership for the Assessment of Readiness for College and Careers (PARCC). The purpose of MC³ is to provide ongoing review, research, and communication related to the implementation and assessment of CCSSM.

The Council's Standards and related work have focused on articulating a rich vision for school mathematics. This vision provided guidance for the development of many state and local standards in the 1990s and the first decade of the new millennium. CCSSM builds on that vision by articulating state standards in detailed form that can be immediately adopted and implemented as state-level curricular frameworks. Despite some differences in the specific content emphases and recommendations, CCSSM and NCTM's standards-related work share a common vision.

The Curriculum Principle in *Principles and Standards for School Mathematics* (NCTM 2000) succinctly captures this perspective: "A curriculum is more than a collection of activities: it must be coherent, focused on important mathematics, and well articulated across the grades" (p. 14). One common characteristic of the shared vision of CCSSM and NCTM is the need to have a curriculum that is *focused*. CCSSM articulates this need through the identification of *critical areas* for kindergarten through grade 8. These areas overlap with the Curriculum Focal Points that NCTM identifies in *Curriculum Focal Points for Prekindergarten through Grade 8 Mathematics* (NCTM 2006). The focus in both cases is on "big ideas" of mathematical content, with specific content clusters targeted at each grade level. "Big ideas are mathematical statements of overarching concepts that are central to a mathematical topic and link numerous smaller mathematical ideas into coherent wholes" (preface, p. viii, to all volumes in NCTM's Essential Understanding Series). Research suggests that a focus on "big ideas" and the development of a holistic understanding improve students' attitudes and engagement in mathematics learning (McREL 2010).

CCSSM and NCTM's work both emphasize the importance of a coherent curriculum. CCSSM, *Curriculum Focal Points*, and *Focus in High School Mathematics*, like *Principles and Standards for School Mathematics*, emphasize the need for a mathematics curriculum that is more than a collection of topics distributed across the years. Ideas at one grade level must build on those from previous years and form the basis for ideas in later years. Lessons must be designed to engage students with particular mathematical ideas in the service of big ideas. The organization of the content across grades must reflect both what is mathematically meaningful and what is known from research and practice about learning mathematics.

CCSSM and NCTM's Standards share a view that important mathematics includes both content and mathematical practices or processes. In this guide, the section "Emphasizing Mathematical Practices and Processes" provides extended discussion of CCSSM's highlighting of mathematical practices and NCTM's focus on mathematical processes. Although slightly different in their details, these practices and processes represent both essential mathematics to be learned and ways in which students engage in learning mathematics content.

Interpreting the Common Core State Standards

Understanding the Common Core State Standards for Mathematics includes knowing what CCSSM contains and how CCSSM relates to familiar guidelines and resources. NCTM materials are useful in making sense of CCSSM's identification of *critical areas, domains,* and *clusters of standards* and connecting these ideas to NCTM's prior work.

Prekindergarten–Grade 8

CCSSM identifies *critical areas* of mathematics that students are expected to learn each year from kindergarten through grade 8. These are the big ideas of school mathematics at each grade level. (CCSSM does not address prekindergarten mathematics.) More learning time should be devoted to the critical areas than to other content. In other parts of this guide, the *standards*—which CCSSM organizes into *clusters* that fall under *domains*—are tied to critical areas.

The critical areas that CCSSM identifies for kindergarten through grade 8 align closely with the Focal Points identified for these levels in *Curriculum Focal Points.* Both critical areas and Curriculum Focal Points are sets of mathematical ideas that students are expected to learn at an indicated grade level. In CCSSM, clusters typically correspond to NCTM Content Standards and one or more Expectations associated with particular Standards, as identified in *Principles and Standards.* Portions of books in the Essential Understanding Series articulate mathematical understanding that can be useful to teachers who are working to help students meet standards of CCSSM.

For each grade level, *Making It Happen* (NCTM 2010) provides a chart that details these relationships among CCSSM's critical areas, the Content Standards and Expectations in *Principles and Standards,* the Focal Points in *Curriculum Focal Points,* and the mathematics for teachers treated in the Essential Understanding Series. Each chart is organized according to the template below. Appendix A includes all of these charts.

In CCSSM, *critical areas* lie alongside *domains,* which contain *clusters* of specific standards.

Go to http://www.nctm.org/more4u and enter the access code printed on this book's title page for a version of Appendix A with live links for NCTM resources.

Interpretation Chart for Each Level, Pre-K–Grade 8

CCSSM Critical Area	Principles and Standards	Curriculum Focal Points	Essential Understanding Series
	For information about instructional goals related to the mathematics content in this critical area	For information about how this content appears within an example of a focused curriculum proposed by NCTM	For an articulation of mathematical understanding that is essential for teachers working in this critical area

An educator who is trying to interpret CCSSM might be most likely to ask, "If my current curriculum was written with NCTM Standards and Focal Points in mind, how do the Common Core Standards relate to those?" The charts in Appendix A answer that question logically by first identifying a CCSSM critical area and then showing how it relates to *Principles and Standards* (the broadest perspective) and *Curriculum Focal Points* (a more targeted perspective). Therefore, the columns in the chart appear in that order from left to right. Because books in the Essential Understanding Series address the placement and development of the content related to the CCSSM critical area, the chart places them in the last column, as a transition to professional development and implementation issues. To view the chart for a particular grade level, see Appendix A.

Grades 9–12

In contrast to the way in which CCSSM presents expectations for kindergarten–grade 8, it does not provide grade-by-grade or course-by-course standards for high school mathematics, nor does it identify or articulate critical areas. Instead, the standards for grades 9–12 are organized by six conceptual categories: number and quantity, algebra, functions, modeling, geometry, and statistics and probability. For each of these categories, other than modeling, CCSSM arranges specific standards into *domains*, each of which contains *clusters* of specific *standards*. Standards related to modeling are incorporated in other conceptual categories.

Conceptual categories contain *domains*, which contain *clusters* of specific standards.

Although *Principles and Standards* also arranges its content guidelines by grade band, its organization is quite different from that of CCSSM. *Principles and Standards* presents five overarching Content Standards that are common across the grade bands, and it breaks each Standard into several areas and gives specific Expectations for each area in a particular grade band.

Focus in High School Mathematics provides guidance about ways to integrate reasoning and sense making into instruction and learning in five content strands across grades 9–12. Reasoning and sense making in each of these strands include several characteristic Key Elements.

The following chart illustrates the very different organizations of CCSSM, *Principles and Standards,* and *Focus in High School Mathematics.* None of the three gives specific grade- or course-level recommendations or critical areas for grades 9–12, although possible "pathways," along which content can be organized, appear in Appendix A of CCSSM.

Organizational Elements of CCSSM, *Principles and Standards,* and *Focus in High School Mathematics*

CCSSM Conceptual Categories	*Principles and Standards* Content Standards	*Focus in High School Mathematics* Content Strands
Number and Quantity --- Algebra Functions Modeling Geometry Statistics and Probability	Number and Operations Measurement Algebra *(included in Algebra)* --- Geometry Data Analysis and Probability	Number and Measurement *(included with Number)* Algebraic Symbols Functions --- Geometry Probability and Statistics
Organized by— - Domains - Clusters - Standards	Organized by— - Areas - Expectations	Organized by— - Key Elements

Making It Happen provides charts, arranged according to the template below, to show the connections in the content of the three sets of guidelines. Five such charts organize information about conceptual categories identified in CCSSM. (The charts omit modeling, the sixth CCSSM conceptual category, which does not have specific standards.)

Interpretation Chart for Each Conceptual Category, Grades 9–12

CCSSM Cluster of Standards Identified by Domain	*Principles and Standards*	*Focus in High School Mathematics*	Essential Understanding Series
	For information about instructional goals related to the mathematics content in this cluster	For information about promoting reasoning and sense making in this cluster	For an articulation of mathematical understanding that is essential for teachers working in this cluster

The content in each chart is organized by clusters within the domains for a conceptual category, as indicated in the first column. Rows in the chart are arranged by either a cluster or a domain, depending on its "grain size." Some domains are relatively specific (e.g., "Vector and Matrix Quantities"), whereas some clusters are quite general (e.g., "Interpret functions that arise in applications in terms of the context").

The second column provides corresponding Expectations from *Principles and Standards*, organized by areas. The third column identifies Key Elements from *Focus in High School Mathematics* that may be useful in understanding possibilities for incorporating reasoning and sense making in the content related to the row's cluster.

The fourth and final column indicates a portion of one or more books in the Essential Understanding Series that articulate mathematical understanding that can benefit teachers in developing the content of this conceptual category. The category Number and Quantity has no corresponding Essential Understanding book, but components of several books in the series are closely related, including chapter 1 of the 9–12 proof and proving book and the vertical articulation issues in chapter 2 of several 6–8 books. To view a sample interpretation chart for the conceptual category of functions, see Appendix A.

Emphasizing Mathematical Practices and Processes

Although CCSSM places significant emphasis on the content that students need to learn in each grade, educators should not regard that content narrowly, as a checklist. Rather, CCSSM stresses that it is essential to connect its Standards for Mathematical Content with its Standards for Mathematical Practice. CCSSM's Standards for Mathematical Practice are closely related to NCTM's Process Standards, as elaborated in *Principles and Standards for School Mathematics* (NCTM 2000). This section explores the relationship between the two.

CCSSM's View of Mathematical Practices

CCSSM emphasizes the need to look beyond specific skills to "'processes and proficiencies' with longstanding importance in mathematics education" (p. 6), explicitly echoing the thinking behind the Process Standards articulated in *Principles and Standards*. The introduction to CCSSM (CCSSI 2010, p. 4) juxtaposes the nature of content standards and the importance of one of the processes—reasoning:

> [CCSSM's] Standards define what students should understand and be able to do in their study of mathematics.... One hallmark of mathematical understanding is the ability to justify, in a way appropriate to the student's mathematical maturity, why a particular mathematical statement is true or where a mathematical rule comes from.

The Standards for Mathematical Practice (CCSSI 2010, pp. 6–8) provide more detailed descriptions of the proficiencies with process that CCSSM advocates for students. As enumerated by CCSSM, students need to be able to do the following:

1. Make sense of problems and persevere in solving them.
2. Reason abstractly and quantitatively.
3. Construct viable arguments and critique the reasoning of others.
4. Model with mathematics.
5. Use appropriate tools strategically.
6. Attend to precision.
7. Look for and make use of structure.
8. Look for and express regularity in repeated reasoning.

The Process Standards in *Principles and Standards,* as well as the Reasoning Habits in *Focus in High School Mathematics,* provide important insights into the Standards for Mathematical Practice in CCSSM.

CCSSM elaborates each of these eight standards in a paragraph and explains that together they describe "varieties of expertise that mathematics educators at all levels should seek to develop in their students" (CCSSI 2010, p. 6). CCSSM also emphasizes the need to connect the Standards for Mathematical Practice with the Standards for Mathematical Content.

NCTM's Longstanding Emphasis on Process

As previously noted, CCSSM makes explicit reference to the Process Standards enunciated in *Principles and Standards*. In fact, when NCTM released this landmark publication in 2000, the Council had already been focusing on mathematical processes for a long time. *An Agenda for Action* (NCTM 1980) emphasized the centrality of mathematical problem solving, and *Curriculum and Evaluation Standards for School Mathematics* (NCTM 1989) described Process Standards for three grade bands.

Principles and Standards describes five Content Standards and five Process Standards that NCTM urges educators to make the focus of school mathematics, prekindergarten–grade 12. The Process Standards—for Problem Solving, Reasoning and Proof, Communication, Connections, and Representation—"highlight ways of acquiring and using content knowledge" (NCTM 2000, p. 29), thus underscoring the close interrelationship of process and content also expressed in CCSSM.

Principles and Standards identifies several major areas of emphasis for each Process Standard, and a chapter devoted to each grade band discusses characteristics of these processes at that level. In addition, NCTM's Navigations Series includes a number of volumes that explore students' development of skill in using particular processes identified by the Process Standards.

NCTM has released two publications since 2000 to provide additional guidance related to *Principles and Standards*: *Curriculum Focal Points for Prekindergarten through Grade 8 Mathematics: A Quest for Coherence* (NCTM 2006) and *Focus in High School Mathematics: Reasoning and Sense Making* (NCTM 2009). Although the Council's intention with *Curriculum Focal Points* was primarily to provide a concise and coherent description of important content for each grade level encapsulated in Focal Points and Connections (links from the Focal Points to other, related ideas), attention to process was embedded within all of those grade-level descriptions.

In contrast, the companion volume for high school, *Focus in High School Mathematics,* maintains a clear focus on the Process Standards—particularly, the Problem Solving Standard and the Reasoning and Proof Standard. This publication provides a detailed list of Reasoning Habits, organized into four major categories: analyzing a problem, seeking and using connections, implementing a strategy, and reflecting on a solution. Recommending that students develop these as a part of the high school mathematics program, the book presents a set of chapters that describe possibilities for embedding opportunities for reasoning and sense making in five major content strands, with examples of the development of the Reasoning Habits.

A Comparison of the CCSSM and NCTM Approaches to Process

A comparison of the Mathematical Practices set forth in CCSSM with both the Process Standards developed in *Principles and Standards* and the Reasoning Habits described in *Focus in High School Mathematics* reveals general alignment between the goals of CCSSM and NCTM's efforts to promote process in mathematics. Table 1 provides an overview. Note that the comparisons are at a very general level, and only some aspects of a Process Standard or category of Reasoning Habits correspond to a particular Standard for Mathematical Practice.

Table 1. General comparison of attention to process in CCSSM, *Principles and Standards*, and *Focus in High School Mathematics*

CCSSM Standards for Mathematical Practice	Principles and Standards Process Standards	Focus in High School Mathematics General Categories of Reasoning Habits
1. Make sense of problems and persevere in solving them.	Problem Solving Communication Representation	Analyzing a problem Seeking and using connections Implementing a strategy Reflecting on a solution
2. Reason abstractly and quantitatively.	Problem Solving Reasoning and Proof	Analyzing a problem
3. Construct viable arguments and critique the reasoning of others.	Reasoning and Proof Communication Representation	Analyzing a problem Implementing a strategy Reflecting on a solution

(continued)

Table 1. (*Continued*)

CCSSM Standards for Mathematical Practice	*Principles and Standards* Process Standards	*Focus in High School Mathematics* General Categories of Reasoning Habits
4. Model with mathematics.	Problem Solving Reasoning and Proof Connections Representation	Analyzing a problem Seeking and using connections Reflecting on a solution
5. Use appropriate tools strategically.	Problem Solving Representation	Analyzing a problem Reflecting on a solution
6. Attend to precision.	Problem Solving Communication	Analyzing a problem Reflecting on a solution
7. Look for and make use of structure.	Problem Solving Reasoning and Proof Connections	Analyzing a problem Implementing a strategy
8. Look for and express regularity in repeated reasoning.	Problem Solving Connections	Analyzing a problem Implementing a strategy

In fact, differences in how the three documents approach mathematical processes are significant. In contrast to the fairly general Process Standards articulated in *Principles and Standards*, CCSSM provides rather specific statements of the processes in which students should engage. *Principles and Standards* paints a broader view of the role of mathematical processes, incorporating some processes that are not explicitly addressed in CCSSM, such as building new mathematical knowledge through problem solving, the first area described within the Problem Solving Standard in *Principles and Standards*.

Although the categories of Reasoning Habits in *Focus in High School Mathematics* are broader than the Mathematical Practices in CCSSM, the individual Reasoning Habits that *Focus in High School Mathematics* details are generally a close match in level of specificity for the descriptions of the Mathematical Practices in CCSSM. For example, in describing Mathematical Practice Standard 3, "Construct viable arguments and critique the reasoning of others," CCSSM states that students "make conjectures and build a logical progression of statements to explore the truth of their conjectures" (CCSSI 2010, p. 6). Similarly, under the category "Reflecting on a solution," *Focus in High School*

Mathematics suggests the Reasoning Habit "making logical deductions based on current progress, verifying conjectures, and extending initial findings" (NCTM 2009, p. 10).

Despite similarities between the Reasoning Habits in *Focus in High School Mathematics* and the Mathematical Practices in CCSSM, the two lists are organized very differently, and each reveals some unique perspectives. For example, CCSSM places somewhat greater emphasis on precision, as evidenced in Mathematical Practice Standard 6, "Attend to precision," which includes the suggestion that students should "try to use clear definitions in discussion with others and in their own reasoning" (CCSSI 2010, p. 7). In contrast, *Focus in High School Mathematics* gives more attention to Reasoning Habits related to statistics, such as "deciding whether a statistical approach is appropriate" (NCTM 2009, p. 9), a habit identified in the category "Analyzing a Problem." Reasoning Habits related to statistics are discussed in more depth in *Focus in High School Mathematics: Statistics and Probability* (Shaughnessy, Chance, and Kranendonk 2009), a volume in NCTM's companion series supporting and extending *Focus in High School Mathematics*.

A more detailed version of table 1 is presented in Appendix B, which shows the connections among the three documents at a finer level. In Appendix B, the statements from the descriptive commentary in the Standards for Mathematical Practice in CCSSM are matched with the areas of emphasis within the Process Standards from *Principles and Standards* and the specific Reasoning Habits from *Focus in High School Mathematics*. Although CCSSM, *Principles and Standards*, and *Focus in High School Mathematics* provide unique ways of describing mathematical processes, the three are united in their emphasis on the importance of mathematical processes, both as a goal and as a means of learning mathematics.

The Six NCTM Principles: The Foundation of a High-Quality Mathematics Program

Principles and Standards for School Mathematics (NCTM 2000) proposes six principles—the Equity, Curriculum, Teaching, Learning, Assessment, and Technology Principles—as a foundation for high-quality mathematics programs. The chart below and the subsequent discussion summarize the main ideas for each Principle. The section titled "Putting the NCTM Principles into Action in Your School" focuses on specific actions that you can take to support these principles in your school.

Equity	Curriculum
Excellence in mathematics education requires equity—high expectations and strong support for all students.	*A curriculum is more than a collection of activities: it must be coherent, focused on important mathematics, and well articulated across the grades.*
• Equity requires high expectations and worthwhile opportunities for all. • Equity requires accommodating differences to help everyone learn mathematics. • Equity requires resources and support for all classrooms and students.	• A mathematics curriculum should be coherent. • A mathematics curriculum should focus on important mathematics. • A mathematics curriculum should be well articulated across the grades.
Teaching	**Learning**
Effective mathematics teaching requires understanding what students know and need to learn and then challenging and supporting them to learn it well.	*Students must learn mathematics with understanding, actively building new knowledge from experience and prior knowledge.*
• Effective teaching requires knowing and understanding mathematics, students as learners, and pedagogical strategies. • Effective teaching requires a challenging and supportive classroom learning environment. • Effective teaching requires continually seeking improvement.	• Learning mathematics with understanding is essential. • Students can learn mathematics with understanding.

Assessment

Assessment should support the learning of important mathematics and furnish useful information to both teachers and students.

- Assessment should enhance students' learning.

- Assessment is a valuable tool for making instructional decisions.

Technology

Technology is essential in teaching and learning mathematics; it influences the mathematics that is taught and enhances students' learning.

- Technology enhances mathematics learning.

- Technology supports effective mathematics teaching.

- Technology influences what mathematics is taught.

Achieving Equity

Wide variation in performance among U.S. schools serving similar students indicates that existing achievement gaps can be closed and that demographic factors are not destiny if students receive high-quality instruction and necessary support (McKinsey & Company 2009). Research indicates that all students can learn mathematics when they have access to high-quality mathematics instruction and are given sufficient time and support to learn the curriculum (Burris, Heubert, and Levin 2006; Campbell 1995; Education Trust 2005; Griffin, Case, and Siegler 1994; Knapp et al. 1995; Silver and Stein 1996; Slavin and Lake 2008; Usiskin 2007).

Traditionally, mathematics has been seen as something that only a select few can master. High-quality mathematics education is no longer just for those who want to study mathematics and science in college—it is required for most postsecondary education programs and careers (see introduction). In addition, CCSSM expects that all students will study and attain the same common core of knowledge and skills. Too many students—especially students who are poor, nonnative speakers of English, disabled, or members of racial minority groups—are victims of low expectations in mathematics. For example, traditional tracking practices have consistently disadvantaged groups of students by relegating them to low-status mathematics classes where they repeat computational skills year after year, fall further and further behind their peers in grade-level courses, and do not experience significant mathematical substance (Boaler, Wiliam, and Brown 2000; Stiff, Johnson, and Akos 2011; Tate and Rousseau 2002). Low-track or slow math instructional groups are a lifetime sentence to the students placed in them, and such groups serve no purpose other than to put students further behind in their study of mathematics. CCSSM—and fundamental social justice—require that all students be held to, and be supported in meeting, the same rigorous standards.

Equity does not mean that all students should have identical instruction or that all students should have the same amount of instructional time. It does mean that reasonable and appropriate accommodations should be made so that all students have the opportunity to experience success in the challenging grade-level mathematics content outlined in CCSSM. For example, some students may need additional instructional time and support to achieve at the level outlined in CCSSM. The encouraging finding is that if students are given enough time and support to master content, the vast majority can achieve at the level of students who learn material quickly (Usiskin 2007). In addition, students with special interest and exceptional talent in mathematics may need and should receive opportunities to be accelerated in the curriculum, enrichment programs, or additional resources to challenge and engage them.

Focusing the Curriculum and Making It Coherent

The traditional mathematics curriculum in the United States has been criticized as "a mile wide and an inch deep." Students study many topics each year—often ones that they covered in previous years, with very little depth added each time that students encounter them. *Curriculum Focal Points* (NCTM 2006) represented the first concerted national effort to bring focus and coherence to the pre-K–grade 8 mathematics curriculum. CCSSM takes this work further, articulating a specific coherent and focused K–8 curriculum with conceptual progressions so that students have the opportunity to learn increasingly sophisticated mathematical ideas as they progress through the grades (Confrey, Maloney, and Nguyen 2010).

The U.S. mathematics curriculum has also been characterized as consisting of too many low-level tasks, reflecting a procedural emphasis without giving students the opportunity to develop deep understanding of conceptual mathematics and solve meaningful problems (Silver 2010). High-performing countries have more cognitively demanding tasks in their curricula and encourage students to focus more on conceptual understanding (Schmidt et al. 2011; Stigler and Hiebert 2004):

> Overall, U.S. students are exposed to a less difficult school mathematics curriculum that places them at a disadvantage when compared to students in many other countries of the world.... [T]he specifics as to which topics and how demanding they are is a substantively important part of a student's learning opportunity.... The consequences are clear—less opportunity to learn challenging mathematics corresponds to lower achievement. (Schmidt et al. 2011, pp. 422–23)

This difference explains much of the achievement differences between students in the United States and students in other, higher-performing countries.

Although NCTM (in, e.g., *Principles and Standards for School Mathematics* [2000]), the National Mathematics Advisory Panel Report (2008), the National Research Council (NRC 2001), and CCSSM all call for a balanced approach to the curriculum (conceptual understanding, problem-solving and reasoning skill, and computational fluency), it is clear that to improve mathematics education and students' mathematics achievement in the United States, curriculum and instruction must place more emphasis on conceptual understanding and problem solving and reasoning (Desimore et al. 2005; Thompson 2008).

Ensuring High-Quality Teaching

Mathematics education has traditionally relied on standards and curricular programs as the primary levers to improve student achievement (Larson 2009). However, student achievement is not solely a function of standards and curriculum (NCTM 2007). Student achievement is more highly correlated with the nature of classroom instruction—how mathematics is taught and how teachers use the curriculum—rather than with what curriculum is used (Slavin and Lake 2008; Stein and Kaufman 2010).

Effective mathematics teaching is a complex endeavor, and there are no easy recipes, nor is there a single, "correct" way to teach mathematics (Hiebert and Grouws 2006, 2007). Effective teachers possess content knowledge, general pedagogical knowledge, and content-specific pedagogical knowledge. For teachers to help students engage in rich and challenging mathematical tasks, they must first have their own deep understanding of the mathematics that they teach. In addition, teachers must understand CCSSM and areas for critical emphasis in the grade that they teach, as well as the grades before and after it. The pedagogical knowledge needed by teachers includes knowing how students learn mathematics, how to build on students' existing knowledge, how to address students' misconceptions, how to present ideas so that students gain deep understanding, and how to assess students' learning.

Teaching practices in the United States have remained virtually unchanged for nearly a century (Baroody 2011; Jacobs et al. 2006; Stigler and Hiebert 1999; Truxaw and DeFranco 2008). This traditional approach to teaching can best be described as a transmission style of teaching. The teacher first checks homework with the class, then briefly demonstrates procedures and states information, and then engages the students in extensive practice of demonstrated procedures. The fact that mathematics teaching has continued to look largely the same is not the fault of teachers. Teaching largely looks the same today as it has for a century because teaching is a cultural activity, and cultural activities are, by definition, extremely resistant to change (Stigler and Hiebert 1999; Stigler and Thompson 2009).

An instructional environment that emphasizes mathematical processes, as outlined in CCSSM's Standards for Mathematical Practice and NCTM's Process Standards, for example, is associated with higher student achievement (Reys et al. 2003; Schoenfeld 2002; Senk and Thompson 2003; Stein and Smith 2010). In 2007, NCTM released a revised and updated second edition of *Professional Standards for Teaching Mathematics* (NCTM 1989), titled *Mathematics Teaching Today: Improving Practice, Improving Student Learning*. This publication outlines seven standards for the teaching of mathematics, organized under three categories—knowledge, implementation, and analysis. Although these seven teaching standards predate CCSSM, their emphasis on the development of students' facility with mathematical processes, as outlined in NCTM's Process Standards, is consistent with instruction that supports the Standards for Mathematical Practice articulated in CCSSM:

Knowledge

1. **Standard 1: Knowledge of Mathematics and General Pedagogy**

   Teachers need to (*a*) have a deep understanding of significant mathematics; (*b*) understand theories of student intellectual development; (*c*) possess knowledge of modes of instruction and assessment; and (*d*) know effective communication and motivational strategies.

2. **Standard 2: Knowledge of Student Mathematical Learning**

   Teachers need to know (*a*) what is known about the ways students learn mathematics; (*b*) various strategies for supporting students when they struggle to make sense of mathematics; (*c*) how to use a variety of tools in mathematical investigations; and (*d*) ways to engage and guide students in the CCSSM Standards for Mathematical Practice and the NCTM Process Standards.

Implementation

3. **Standard 3: Worthwhile Mathematical Tasks**

   Teachers need to (*a*) design learning experiences and pose tasks that engage students' intellect; (*b*) develop both students' mathematical understandings and their skills; (*c*) encourage students to make mathematical connections and develop understanding of the big ideas of mathematics; (*d*) call for problem formulation, problem solving, and reasoning; (*e*) promote communication about mathematics; and (*f*) draw on students' diverse backgrounds, experiences, and dispositions.

4. **Standard 4: Learning Environment**

Teachers need to create a learning environment that provides (*a*) the time necessary to investigate significant mathematics; (*b*) an atmosphere of respect and value for students' ideas and ways of thinking; (*c*) a climate that invites students to take intellectual risks in raising questions and formulating conjectures; and (*d*) encouragement for participation in mathematical discourse.

5. **Standard 5: Discourse**

Teachers need to orchestrate mathematical discourse by (*a*) posing questions and tasks that elicit, engage, and challenge students' thinking; (*b*) listening carefully to students' ideas and deciding what to pursue in depth from among the ideas students generate during a discussion; (*c*) asking students to clarify and justify their ideas orally and in writing; (*d*) deciding when and how to attach mathematical notation and language to students' ideas; (*e*) encouraging and accepting the use of multiple representations; (*f*) deciding when to provide information, when to clarify an issue, when to model, when to lead, and when to let students productively struggle; and (*g*) monitoring students' participation in discussion and deciding when and how to encourage each student to participate.

Analysis

6. **Standard 6: Reflection on Student Learning**

Teachers need to (*a*) engage in ongoing analysis of students' learning to ensure that every student is meeting grade-level standards and is developing a positive disposition toward mathematics; (*b*) adapt or modify tasks while teaching; (*c*) describe and comment on each student's learning to parents and administrators; and (*d*) provide regular feedback to students.

7. **Standard 7: Reflection on Teaching Practice**

Teachers should engage in ongoing analysis of their own teaching by (*a*) reflecting regularly on what and how they teach; (*b*) examining effects of the task, discourse, and learning environment on students' development; (*c*) seeking to improve their teaching and practice by participating in professional learning communities beyond their classroom; (*d*) analyzing and using assessment data to make reasoned decisions about necessary changes in curriculum; and (*e*) collaborating with colleagues in professional learning communities and other structures to improve instructional programs.

Enriching Learning

NCTM has long argued that mathematical proficiency has multiple strands, but learning mathematics with understanding is the cornerstone of NCTM's vision for mathematics education. Similarly, CCSSM states that "mathematical understanding and procedural skill are equally important" but stresses conceptual understanding of key ideas and organizing principles to structure essential big ideas (CCSSI 2010, p. 4). Learning with understanding is essential to mathematical literacy. The word *literacy* probably makes many of us think of reading. Not only does reading literacy mean being able to pronounce and decode words, but it also means being able to comprehend and understand what one reads. Reading literacy is analogous to mathematical literacy, which involves having procedural and computational skills as well as conceptual understanding and possessing the ability to draw on both to make sense of and solve mathematical problems. Teaching for understanding engages students naturally in the CCSSM Standards for Mathematical Practice.

Over a decade ago, the National Research Council (2001) defined mathematical proficiency as consisting of five interwoven and interdependent strands. This remains the widely accepted definition of mathematical proficiency (Baroody 2011):

1. **Understanding** (Conceptual Understanding): Comprehending mathematical concepts, operations, and relations—knowing what mathematical symbols, diagrams, and procedures mean.

2. **Computing** (Procedural Fluency): Carrying out mathematical procedures, such as adding, subtracting, multiplying, and dividing numbers flexibly, accurately, efficiently, and appropriately.

3. **Applying** (Strategic Competence): Being able to formulate problems mathematically and to devise strategies for solving them by using concepts and procedures appropriately.

4. **Reasoning** (Adaptive Reasoning): Using logic to explain and justify a solution to a problem or to extend from something not yet known.

5. **Engaging** (Productive Disposition): Seeing mathematics as sensible, useful, and doable—if one works at it—and being willing to do the work.

Research indicates that debates about the relative importance of procedural and conceptual knowledge—often one of the main issues in the previous decade's "math wars"—are pointless and create a false dichotomy (Baroody, Feil, and Johnson 2007; NMAP 2008; NRC 2001). Both dimensions of learning mathematics are important, and a certain amount of conceptual knowledge is necessary to develop deep procedural knowledge, and vice versa (Baroody, Feil, and Johnson 2007; NMAP 2008; NRC 2001).

Although there is general agreement that all the strands are important, it is also generally recommended that to improve mathematics education in the United States, more emphasis needs to be placed on conceptual understanding (Desimore et al. 2005; Thompson 2008). Learning without understanding has long been a too-common outcome of school mathematics instruction. In too many cases, students are simply instructed to mimic rules or procedures demonstrated by their teacher without much depth or understanding. For students to be successful in meeting the expectations of CCSSM, this traditional learning emphasis must change in favor of NCTM's and CCSSM's vision of learning with understanding, as articulated in the NCTM Process Standards and CCSSM Standards for Mathematical Practice.

Assessing Appropriately

Used appropriately, assessment is an essential tool in any mathematics program to improve teaching and learning. Unfortunately, since the advent of No Child Left Behind (NCLB 2002), much of the assessment focus has been on preparing students for state accountability tests. In too many cases, this focus has resulted in a narrowing of the curriculum, since many state accountability tests are limited in the scope of what they test. Consequently, they do not always provide an accurate view of students' conceptual understanding or their problem-solving skills—goals of both NCTM and CCSSM. As CCSSM states, "Mathematical understanding and procedural skill are equally important" (CCSSI 2010, p. 4). Both CCSSM assessment consortia (PARCC and SBAC) intend to design new assessments that are consistent with the vision of CCSSM and NCTM to assess reasoning and sense making, problem solving, and conceptual understanding. If the assessments take this form, then these new assessments will go beyond many current state tests, which frequently assess low-level procedural skills. Past improvements in scores on state accountability tests therefore may not reflect actual student improvement in the broader set of skills that today's students need and that are called for by CCSSM and NCTM.

Over a decade ago, the National Council of Teachers of Mathematics recommended that formative assessment assume a larger role in mathematics instruction and be used as a tool to make instructional decisions and improve student learning:

> Assessment should be more than merely a test at the end of instruction to see how students perform under special conditions; rather, it should be an integral part of instruction that informs and guides teachers as they make instructional

decisions. Assessment should not merely be done *to* students; rather, it should also be done *for* students, to guide and enhance their learning. (NCTM 2000, p. 22)

The authors of the National Mathematics Advisory Panel Report recommended the use of regular (weekly) formative assessments of students as a key strategy to support all students—particularly those who struggle in mathematics—provided that the results of those assessments be used to shape targeted additional instruction and support based on student progress (NMAP 2008). This recommendation was based on the abundant research on effective instructional interventions in mathematics and the power of formative assessment to improve student achievement (Baker, Gersten, and Lee 2002; Hanley 2005; Marzano 2006; McCall et al. 2006; Popham 2008; Wiliam 2007; Wiliam and Thompson 2007; Williams 2003).

A meta-analysis of the research on formative assessment found that student gains as a result of formative assessment are "amongst the largest ever reported for educational interventions" (Black and Wiliam 1998, p. 61). Popham (2008) defines formative assessment as "a planned process in which assessment-elicited evidence of students' status is used by teachers to adjust their ongoing instructional procedures or by students to adjust their current learning tactics" (p. 6). An important point is that what makes an assessment formative or not is whether the results are used to modify and adapt instruction (Wiliam 2007). With this in mind, it is possible that nearly every assessment, whether it is designed to be formative or summative, can serve a formative function if teachers use the results to modify and guide future instruction.

Formative assessment should be part of mathematics teachers' daily practice and be viewed as an ongoing process during lessons and not just as an instrument that is administered periodically. Assessments before, during, and after instruction allow teachers to make appropriate decisions about such considerations as reviewing material, reteaching a difficult concept, or providing additional or more challenging material for students who are struggling or who need enrichment. Students show what they know and can do in different ways. Relying on only one form of assessment, whether formative or summative, may give an incomplete picture of students' actual depth of understanding. Therefore, when using assessments, teachers should include open-ended items, constructive-response tasks, selected-response items, performance tasks, observations, discussions, journals, and portfolios aimed at assessing students' depth of understanding—not just their procedural competence.

Formative assessment in particular can take many forms and does not have to be limited to formal lessons or weekly quizzes (Popham 2008). Observations of students working in groups and of classroom discourse can provide a teacher with useful and continuous information regarding students' developing levels of understanding as a lesson unfolds. The most important point is that "the available research evidence suggests that considerable enhancements in student achievement are possible when teachers use assessment, minute-by-minute and day-by-day, to adjust their instruction to meet their students' learning needs.... Students are more engaged in class, achieve higher standards, and teachers find their work more professionally fulfilling" as a result of efforts to embed ongoing formative assessment in instruction (Wiliam 2007, p. 4). In all likelihood, if teachers were to devote more attention and effort to using formative assessment to improve instruction, they would need to devote less instructional time to summative test-preparation activities, could achieve a broader set of learning goals, and would see results on large-scale summative assessments simultaneously improve. Quality mathematics instructional practices and preparation for large-scale assessments do not have to be perceived as mutually exclusive (Martin et al. 2011).

Teaching with Technology

Students should have access to a full range of technological tools. Teaching with such tools supports CCSSM Standard for Mathematical Practice 5: "Use appropriate tools strategically" (CCSSI 2010, p. 7). "The research evidence makes it clear that students can learn more mathematics more deeply with the appropriate use of technology (Battista 2010; Heid and Blume 2008). The teacher plays the central role in ensuring that technology is used appropriately—to support students' learning of mathematics—not as a crutch or a replacement for the mastery of basic concepts and skills. The depth of problem solving that students can pursue with proper use of technology is astounding. Technology can provide powerful visual images of mathematical ideas, can help organize and analyze data, and can efficiently and accurately perform mathematical computations and symbolic manipulations so that students can focus on conceptual understanding and higher-order thinking. Preparing all students to use technological tools that are available to them is also essential for success in the workplace and in our knowledge-based and increasingly technology-based society.

Examples of High-Quality Mathematics Classrooms

The following elementary, middle, and high school classroom scenarios illustrate high-quality mathematics teaching and learning and the CCSSM Standards for Mathematical Practice.

Elementary School Classroom Example

Consider the interchange that occurred in an upper elementary class between a teacher and her students, who explained how they divided nine brownies equally among eight people (NCTM 2000, pp. 186–87):

Sarah:	The first four, we cut them in half. [*Jasmine divides squares in half on an overhead transparency.*]
Ms. Carter:	Now as you explain, could you explain why you did it in half?
Sarah:	Because when you put it in half, it becomes four … four … eight halves.
Ms. Carter:	Eight halves. What does that mean if there are eight halves?
Sarah:	Then each person gets a half.
Ms. Carter:	Okay, that each person gets a half. [*Jasmine labels halves 1 through 8 for each of the eight people.*]
Sarah:	Then there were five boxes [*brownies*] left. We put them in eighths.
Ms. Carter:	Okay, so they divided them into eighths. Could you tell us why you chose eighths?
Sarah:	It's easiest. Because then everyone will get … each person will get a half and [*addresses Jasmine*] … how many eighths?
Jasmine:	[*Quietly*] Five-eighths.
Ms. Carter:	I didn't know why you did it in eighths. That's the reason. I just wanted to know why you chose eighths.
Jasmine:	We did eighths because then if we did eighths, each person would get each eighth, I mean one-eighth out of each brownie.
Ms. Carter:	OK, one-eighth out of each brownie. Can you just, you don't have to number, but just show us what you mean by that? I heard the words, but…

(continued)

> *Jasmine:* [*Shades in one-eighth of each of the five brownies that were divided into eighths.*] Person 1 would get this … [*points to one-eighth*].
>
> *Ms. Carter:* Oh, out of each brownie.
>
> *Sarah:* Out of each brownie, one person will get one-eighth.
>
> *Ms. Carter:* One-eighth. OK. So how much then did they get if they got their fair share?
>
> *Jasmine and Sarah:* They got a half and five-eighths.
>
> *Ms. Carter:* Do you want to write that down at the top, so I can see what you did? [*Jasmine writes* 1/2 + 1/8 + 1/8 + 1/8 + 1/8 + 1/8 *at the top of the overhead transparency.*]

Middle School Classroom Example

Students in a middle-grades classroom were working in pairs to determine the dimensions of a rectangle, given the ratio of the length to width and the area (NCTM 2000, pp. 268–70):

The students began by working collaboratively in pairs to solve the following problem, adapted from Bennett, Maier, and Nelson (1998):

> A certain rectangle has length and width that are whole numbers of inches, and the ratio of its length to its width is 4 to 3. Its area is 300 square inches. What are its length and width?

As the students worked on the problem, the teacher circulated around the room, monitoring the work of the pairs and responding to their questions. She also noted different approaches that were used by the students and made decisions about which students she would ask to present solutions.

After most students had a chance to solve the problem, the teacher asked Lee and Randy to present their method. They proceeded to the overhead projector to explain their work. After briefly restating the problem, Lee indicated that 3 times 4 is equal to 12 and that they needed "a number that both 3 and 4 would go into." The teacher asked why they had multiplied 3 by 4. Randy replied that the ratio of the length to the width was given as "4 to 3" in the problem. Lee went on to say that they had determined that

(continued)

"3 goes into 15 five times and that 4 goes into 20 five times." Since 15 times 20 is equal to 300, the area of the given rectangle, they concluded that 15 inches and 20 inches were the width and length of the rectangle.

The teacher asked if there were questions for Lee or Randy. Echoing the teacher's query during the presentation of the solution, Tyronne said that he did not understand their solution, particularly where the 12 had come from and how they knew it would help solve the problem. Neither Lee nor Randy was able to explain why they had multiplied 3 by 4 or how the result was connected to their solution. The teacher then indicated that she also wondered how they had obtained the 15 and the 20. The boys reiterated that they had been looking for a number "that both 3 and 4 went into." In reply, Darryl asked how the boys had obtained the number 5. Lee and Randy responded that 5 was what "3 and 4 go into." At this point, Keisha said "Did you guys just guess and check?" Lee and Randy responded in unison, "Yeah!" Although Lee and Randy's final answer was correct and although it contained a kernel of good mathematical insight, their explanation of their solution method left other students confused.

To address the confusion generated by Lee and Randy, the teacher decided to solicit another solution. Because the teacher had seen Rachel and Keisha use a different method, she asked them to explain their approach. Keisha made a sketch of a rectangle, labeling the length 4 and the width 3. She explained that the 4 and 3 were not really the length and width of the rectangle but that the numbers helped remind her about the ratio. Then Rachel explained that she could imagine 12 squares inside the rectangle because 3 times 4 is equal to 12, and she drew lines to subdivide the rectangle accordingly. Next she explained that the area of the rectangle must be equally distributed in the 12 "inside" squares. Therefore, they divided 300 by 12 to determine that each square contains 25 square inches. At the teacher's suggestion, Rachel wrote a 25 in each square in the diagram to make this point clear. Keisha then explained that in order to find the length and width of the rectangle, they had to determine the length of the side of each small square. She argued that since the area of each square was 25 square inches, the side of each square was 5 inches. Then, referring to the diagram [she had drawn], she explained that the length of the rectangle was 20 inches, since it consisted of the sides of four squares. Similarly, the width was found to be 15 inches. To clarify their understanding of the solution, a few students asked questions, which were answered well by Keisha and Rachel.

High School Classroom Example

Students in a high school classroom were determining the shortest leash possible for a dog to guard a yard shaped like a right triangle (NCTM 2000, pp. 354–57):

The students in Mr. Robinson's tenth-grade mathematics class suspect they are in for some interesting problem solving when he starts class with this story: "I have a dilemma. As you may know, I have a faithful dog and a yard shaped like a right triangle. When I go away for short periods of time, I want Fido to guard the yard. Because I don't want him to get loose, I want to put him on a leash and secure the leash somewhere on the lot. I want to use the shortest leash possible, but wherever I secure the leash, I need to make sure the dog can reach every corner of the lot. Where should I secure the leash?"

After Mr. Robinson responds to the usual array of questions and comments (such as "Do you really have a dog?" "Only a math teacher would have a triangle-shaped lot—or notice that the lot was triangular!" "What type of dog is it?"), he asks the students to work in groups of three. All their usual tools, including compass, straightedge, calculator, and computer with geometry software, are available. They are to come up with a plan to solve the problem.

Jennifer dives into the problem right away, saying, "Let's make a sketch using the computer." With her group's agreement, she produces the sketch shown above on the right.

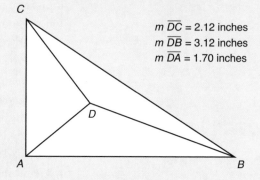

Jennifer's computer-drawn sketch of the "dog in the yard" problem

$m\,\overline{DC}$ = 2.12 inches
$m\,\overline{DB}$ = 3.12 inches
$m\,\overline{DA}$ = 1.70 inches

As Mr. Robinson circulates around the room, he observes each group long enough to monitor its progress. On his first pass, Jennifer's group seems to be experimenting somewhat randomly with dragging the point D to various places, but on his second pass, their work seems more systematic. To assess what members of the group understand, he asks how they are doing:

Mr. R: Joe, can you bring me up-to-date on the progress of your group?

Joe: We're trying to find out where to put the point.

(continued)

Jeff: We don't want the point too close to the corners of the triangle.

Jennifer: I get it! We want all the lengths to be equal! They all work against each other.

Before moving on to work with other groups, Mr. Robinson works with the members of Jennifer's group on clarifying their ideas, using more standard mathematical language, and checking with one another for shared understanding. Jennifer clarifies her idea, and the group decides that it seems reasonable. They set a goal of finding the position for D that results in the line segments DA, DB, and DC all being the same length. When Mr. Robinson returns, the group has concluded that point D has to be the midpoint of the hypotenuse, otherwise, they say, it could not be equidistant from B and C. (Mr. Robinson notes to himself that the group's conclusion is not adequately justified, but he decides not to intervene at this point; the work they will do later in creating a proof will ensure that they examine this reasoning.)

Mr. R: What else would you need to know?

Jeff: We're not sure yet whether D is the same distance from all three vertices.

Jennifer: It has to be! At least I think it is. It looks like it's the center of a circle.

Small-group conversations continue until several groups have made observations and conjectures similar to those made in Jennifer's group. Mr. Robinson pulls the class back together to discuss the problem. When the students converge on a conjecture, he writes it on the board as follows:

Conjecture: The midpoint of the hypotenuse of a right triangle is equidistant from the three vertices of the triangle.

He then asks the students to return to their groups and work toward providing either a proof or a counterexample. The groups continue to work on the problem, settling on proofs and selecting group members to present them on the overhead projector. As always, Mr. Robinson emphasizes the fact that there might be a number of different ways to prove the conjecture.

Remembering Mr. Robinson's mantra about placing the coordinate system to "make things eeeasy," one group places the coordinates as shown in diagram (a) (see p. 34), yielding a common distance of

$$\sqrt{a^2 + b^2}.$$

Alfonse, who is explaining this solution, proudly remarks that it reminds him of the Pythagorean theorem. Mr. Robinson builds on that observation, noting to the class that if the students drop a perpendicular from M to $\overline{AC}$, each of the two right triangles that result has legs of length a and b; thus the lengths of the hypotenuses, MC and MA, are indeed

$$\sqrt{a^2 + b^2}.$$

(continued)

Jennifer's group returns to her earlier comment about the three points A, B, and C being on a circle. After lengthy conversations with, and questions from, Mr. Robinson, that group produces a second proof based on the properties of inscribed angles (diagram [b]).

Diagrams corresponding to two proofs of the midpoint-of-hypotenuse theorem

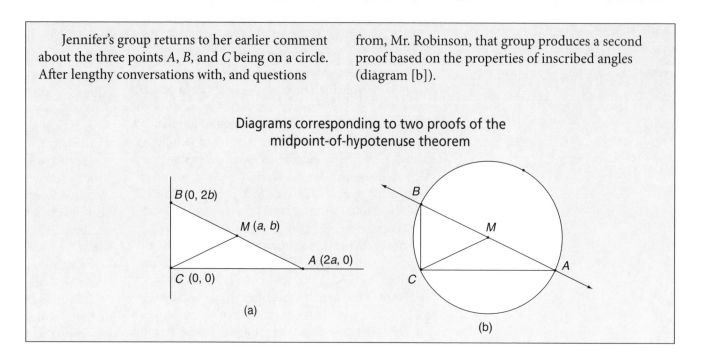

(a)

(b)

Elements of High-Quality Classrooms

These examples illustrate some of the Standards for Mathematical Practice and some of the elements of a classroom—whether it be elementary, middle, or high school—in which high-quality mathematics instruction and learning are taking place.

What are students doing?

- Actively engaging in the learning process (Standard for Mathematical Practice 1)

- Using existing mathematical knowledge to make sense of the task (Standards for Mathematical Practice 1–3)

- Making connections among mathematical concepts (Standards for Mathematical Practice 2, 7, and 8)

- Reasoning and making conjectures about the problem (Standards for Mathematical Practice 1 and 2)

- Communicating their mathematical thinking orally and in writing (Standards for Mathematical Practice 3 and 6)

- Listening and reacting to others' thinking and solutions to problems (Standard for Mathematical Practice 3)

- Using a variety of representations, such as pictures, tables, graphs, and words, for their mathematical thinking (Standard for Mathematical Practice 4)

- Using mathematical and technological tools, such as physical materials, calculators, and computers, along with textbooks and other instructional materials (Standard for Mathematical Practice 5)

- Building new mathematical knowledge through problem solving (Standards for Mathematical Practice 1–8)

What is the teacher doing?

- Choosing "good" problems—ones that invite exploration of an important mathematical concept and allow students the chance to solidify and extend their knowledge (Standards for Mathematical Practice 1, 4, 7, and 8)

- Assessing students' understanding by listening to discussions and asking students to justify their responses (Standards for Mathematical Practice 3 and 6)

- Using questioning techniques to facilitate learning (Standards for Mathematical Practice 3 and 6)

- Encouraging students to explore multiple solutions (Standards for Mathematical Practice 7 and 8)

- Challenging students to think more deeply about the problems they are solving and to make connections with other ideas within mathematics (Standards for Mathematical Practice 1, 2, 7, and 8)

- Creating a variety of opportunities, such as group work and class discussions, for students to communicate mathematically (Standards for Mathematical Practice 3 and 6)

- Modeling appropriate mathematical language and a disposition for solving challenging mathematical problems (Standards for Mathematical Practice 1, 3, 4, and 6)

Although the content changes as students progress through the grades, the statements mentioned above for teachers and students are common characteristics that you should see in any mathematics classroom. In all these

Examples of High-Quality Mathematics Classrooms

scenarios, the teacher has created a climate that supports mathematical thinking and communication (Standards for Mathematical Practice 2 and 3). Students are accustomed to explaining their ideas and questioning solutions that might not make sense to them (Standard for Mathematical Practice 3). Students are not afraid to take risks and know that it is acceptable to struggle with some ideas and to make mistakes (Standard for Mathematical Practice 1). The teacher responds in ways that keep the focus on thinking and reasoning rather than only on getting the right answer (Standard for Mathematical Practice 2). Incorrect answers and ideas are not simply judged wrong. The teacher helps students identify parts of their thinking that may be correct, sometimes leading students to new ideas and solutions that are correct.

> The teacher has created a climate that supports mathematical thinking and communication.

In all three of the foregoing classroom examples, the very important role that the teacher plays is evident. While giving students plenty of opportunities to think for themselves and come up with their own solutions, the teacher is crucial to facilitating and guiding the mathematical tasks and conversations. Achieving this kind of classroom requires much skill and judgment on the part of the teacher, as well as a solid understanding of the mathematics content. It also requires schoolwide changes and support for classroom teachers. The following section discusses six guiding principles that you and your teachers can use to improve mathematics education in your school.

Putting the NCTM Principles into Action in Your School

NCTM's six Principles for school mathematics—Equity, Curriculum, Teaching, Learning, Assessment, and Technology—are the basic precepts that are fundamental to a high-quality mathematics program. Thinking about these Principles and ways in which they can be supported—both schoolwide, by administrators and leaders, and at the classroom level, by individual teachers—is an important step in improving mathematics education in your school.

How Administrators Can Support the Principles

The role of the teacher is central to a high-quality mathematics program. However, many decisions made outside the classroom affect the teacher's ability to carry out the vision of NCTM and CCSSM. As an administrator, your leadership is invaluable in this effort by shaping the instructional mission and focus in your school, providing for the professional development of teachers, designing and implementing supportive policies, and prioritizing the allocation of scarce resources to critical subjects like mathematics, language arts, and science.

Consider the six Principles as you engage in decision making that affects school mathematics. For these Principles to be achieved at the classroom level, the school environment must be structured to encourage and support them. The following are some actions that you can take to support each of the Principles (Mirra 2003; NCSM 2008).

Principle	Key Questions	Actions
Equity: Excellence in mathematics education requires equity—high expectations and strong support for all students.	• Do all students have access to high-quality mathematics instruction and courses? • Do all teachers have high expectations for all students and work collaboratively to erase inequities?	• Create a school climate built on the expectation of high achievement by all students. • Energize teachers and students in ways that challenge current expectations. • Evaluate the processes for placing students in mathematics classes to ensure equal access. • Ensure that all students are in grade-level courses (as specified in CCSSM) and provide additional instructional supports to students who need them to be successful. • Evaluate teacher assignment processes to ensure that all students have access to high-quality instruction.

Principle	Key Questions	Actions
Curriculum: A curriculum is more than a collection of activities; it must be coherent, focused on important mathematics, and well articulated across the grades.	• Are effective instructional materials, aligned with CCSSM and NCTM's vision for school mathematics, adopted, implemented with fidelity, and accepted? • Does the curriculum emphasize both mathematical content and mathematical practices?	• Ensure that each teacher understands CCSSM. • Establish objective and careful processes that involve teachers and teacher leaders in the selection of materials aligned with CCSSM. • Ensure that each teacher implements the adopted curriculum as intended. • Help families and the community at large understand the goals of the curriculum.
Teaching: Effective mathematics teaching requires understanding what students know and need to learn and then challenging them to learn it well.	• Does every teacher know and implement research-based and effective instructional strategies? • Do teachers collaborate to improve instruction?	• Support sustained and ongoing professional development that is tied to the curriculum and that increases teachers' knowledge of mathematics and pedagogy. • Provide teachers with sufficient time to collaborate in professional learning communities (PLCs). • Support teachers in self-evaluation and in analyzing their teaching with colleagues. • Recruit and hire qualified teachers of mathematics. • Make teaching assignments based on the qualifications/effectiveness of teachers. • Spend time in mathematics classrooms and look for instruction based on the CCSSM Standards for Mathematical Practice and the NCTM Process Standards. • Support teacher leaders in mathematics. • Support teachers' attendance at professional conferences.

(continued)

Principle	Key Questions	Actions
Learning: Students must learn mathematics with understanding, actively building new knowledge from experience and prior knowledge.	• Do all students have sufficient time and opportunities to learn mathematics with understanding?	• Ensure that sufficient time is allocated for mathematics instruction. • Ensure that students who need more time and support to learn mathematics receive it. • Protect instructional time. • Promote the importance of learning with understanding to teachers and families. • Develop a plan to identify students who are struggling in mathematics, and implement appropriate interventions.
Assessment: Assessment should support the learning of important mathematics and furnish useful information to both teachers and students.	• Does every teacher use collaboratively designed assessments aligned with CCSSM to monitor student progress?	• Ensure that every teacher uses formative assessment processes to modify and adapt instruction. • Ensure that every teacher is using a variety of assessment methods to measure conceptual understanding, procedural fluency, and problem-solving skill. • Monitor the effect of high-stakes testing on the instructional environment. • Ensure that every teacher uses summative assessment data to evaluate course and program effectiveness.
Technology: Technology is essential in teaching and learning mathematics; it influences the mathematics that is taught and enhances students' learning.	• Is technology used as a tool to enhance student attainment of CCSSM, or is it implemented as a goal in and of itself?	• Ensure that technology is used to enhance learning. • Ensure that students have equitable access to technology. • Support professional development to help teachers implement technology as a support to mathematics instruction.

Observing and Evaluating a Mathematics Classroom

What should you look for when observing a mathematics classroom? The earlier section "Examples of High-Quality Mathematics Classrooms" presented vignettes from elementary, middle, and high school classrooms to illustrate some of the things that you should observe in the classroom.

**Putting the NCTM
Principles into Action
in Your School**

You should look for evidence that teachers are implementing the six NCTM Principles—Equity, Curriculum, Teaching, Learning, Assessment, and Technology— when observing a mathematics classroom. In addition, you should look for an instructional emphasis on the five NCTM Process Standards and the eight CCSSM Standards for Mathematical Practice. The key question to ask is, "Are students developing mathematical proficiency through an instructional emphasis on the mathematical practice and process standards?" If you observe mathematics instruction that exhibits a process-oriented emphasis, the likelihood is that the teacher is focused on developing students' mathematical understanding.

Recent accountability requirements have led to an increase in the inclusion of, or experimenting with the inclusion of, students' test scores and "value-added" measures as significant components of teacher evaluation systems. Research on such evaluation systems is only now emerging, and recent findings raise concerns about the validity of this practice (Corcoran 2010). It is important not to lose sight of the fact that teaching is a complex endeavor, consisting of multiple domains of professional practice, and that student learning is a product not only of what goes on inside the classroom, but also of what goes on outside the classroom. For example, all teachers do not teach under the same working conditions but instead work with differing assignments, student characteristics, and resources. Although evidence of student learning can and should be considered as a factor in the evaluation of teachers, it should be only one factor among many. Comprehensive systems of evaluation of teachers of mathematics should focus on the following domains of professional practice (Danielson 2007; Sawada et al. 2000):

- **Lesson planning.** Does the teacher plan cognitively demanding tasks that take into account the prior knowledge of his or her students? Does the teacher plan lessons that are part of a coherent and well-articulated curriculum that supports student attainment of CCSSM?

- **Lesson implementation and instruction.** Does the teacher implement lesson plans with an emphasis on the fundamental processes of mathematics, as articulated in NCTM's Process Standards and CCSSM's Standards for Mathematical Practice? Does the teacher engage students cognitively through effective questioning and discussion? Does the teacher use information from classroom-based formative assessment processes to monitor and adjust instruction?

- **Demonstrated content knowledge and pedagogical content knowledge.** Does the teacher have a deep understanding of the mathematics content that he or she teaches? Does the teacher design meaningful tasks with an awareness of prerequisite mathematical relationships and knowledge of the learning progressions in CCSSM? Does the teacher identify common barriers to learning and use multiple strategies intended to teach for understanding?

40

Interpreting the Common Core State Standards to Improve Mathematics Education

- **Classroom culture.** Does the teacher create a classroom environment that is respectful of student thinking and discourse and characterized by high expectations and support for all students? Is the classroom environment infused with the teacher's belief in the ability of all students to learn? Is it a culture that encourages discussion of and values a variety of solution strategies and representations?

- **Professionalism.** Does the teacher demonstrate a commitment to his or her own continued learning, and is the teacher a reflective practitioner? Does the teacher examine his or her own practice critically? Does the teacher actively and regularly participate as a constructive member of a professional learning community within his or her own building or school district?

Developing and Supporting Professional Development

One of the most effective ways to have a positive impact on mathematics achievement for all students in your school is by making a substantial investment in professional development. National and international studies of students' achievement highlight the importance of staffing schools with teachers who are properly prepared to teach mathematics. Despite the many myths that teaching talent is something that one is "born with," the ability to teach is in fact learned and continuously refined over time. Teachers, like all other professionals, need ongoing and sustained professional development opportunities throughout their careers. Unfortunately, all too often, professional development for teachers consists of disjointed, occasional workshops and in-service days.

In the new era introduced by CCSSM, this type of professional development is woefully inadequate. Effective professional development must be sustained and embedded within teachers' daily work and focused on the concrete tasks of teaching (Darling-Hammond 2010). Doerr, Goldsmith, and Lewis (2010) outlined the core goals of effective mathematics professional development and the features of professional development programs that support those goals.

Goals of mathematics professional development

The goals of professional development focus on the skills that effective teachers use inside and outside the classroom:

- **Build teachers' mathematical knowledge and their capacity to use it in practice.** Research indicates that teachers' mathematical knowledge predicts gains in student achievement and that professional development that builds this knowledge and the capacity to use it in instruction is more effective than professional development that focuses only on pedagogy.

- **Build teachers' capacity to notice, analyze, and respond to students' thinking.** Professional development that supports teachers in attending to students' thinking shifts teachers' instructional focus from evaluating students' responses to analyzing the depth of their understanding.

- **Build teachers' productive habits of mind.** Professional development programs need to develop in teachers a disposition to attend to their own continual growth and their need to continually improve their practice.

- **Build collegial relationships and structures that support continued learning.** The importance of teacher collaboration with their colleagues is increasingly cited in the research. Too many teachers work in isolation and meet with other teachers only to discuss administrative details. This isolation in turn results in too much inconsistency in the quality of mathematics instruction within schools and districts (Morris and Hiebert 2011). Teachers in high-performing countries—for example, Japan and China—have workdays that include time for extensive collaboration with colleagues (Ma 1999; Stigler and Hiebert 1999). Teachers need to be given the opportunity to collaborate with colleagues who teach the same grade level or mathematics course on a regular basis.

One recent reform in the United States designed to secure this time for teachers is the professional learning community concept (DuFour et al. 2004, 2006). As Schmoker (2006) has written, "professional learning communities have emerged as arguably the best, most agreed-upon means by which to continuously improve instruction and student performance.... [T]he concurrence of the research community on this approach is quite remarkable" (p. 106).

However, teacher collaboration does not always lead to professional learning or instructional improvement and too often is characterized by little more than the sharing of materials and story swapping (Stein, Russell, and Smith 2011). The evidence suggests that it can take up to three years for teachers to begin to work together effectively when implementing structures such as lesson study (Perry and Lewis 2010). As a mathematics education leader, not only do you have the opportunity to establish professional learning communities, but you also have an obligation to ensure that professional learning communities are focused on improving instruction and student learning.

Focusing professional learning communities on intense lesson planning has been demonstrated to be a high-leverage strategy for effecting change in teachers' practice, with the potential to lead to more in-depth interactions within professional learning communities (Perry and Lewis, 2010; Stein, Russell, and Smith 2011). Recent research indicates that effective instruction rests in part on careful planning and that time invested in intensive planning may improve instructional quality (Morris, Hiebert, and Spitzer 2009). Focusing on the CCSSM critical content topics is a productive way to prioritize teachers' collaborative lesson-planning work. Professional learning communities also need to follow specific protocols, and it is essential that these be adhered to for this professional development structure to be effective (see DuFour et al. [2006]).

The bottom line is that professional learning communities must focus on instruction to improve student learning. For an administrator, this means ensuring that all teachers possess an understanding of CCSSM (especially the grade-level areas for critical emphasis); implement instructional practices that emphasize CCSSM's Standards for Mathematical Practice and NCTM's Process Standards; collaboratively design, implement, and reflect on lessons; collaboratively design and use common formative assessment processes and summative assessments; and collaboratively develop action plans to implement when students demonstrate that they have or have not attained the standards set by CCSSM.

Features that support professional development goals

The essential features of programs that achieve the goals for effective professional development are essentially time, support, and opportunities:

- **Substantial investment of time.** The research is clear that the duration of professional development programs has an impact on their effectiveness, including changes in teachers' mathematical knowledge and beliefs, and the creation of collaborative structures. Research indicates that effective professional development programs allow somewhere between 30 and 100 hours of contact time with teachers over the course of six to twelve months (Darling-Hammond et al. 2009).

- **Systemic support.** The degree to which you as an administrator support the particular professional development program, whether it be professional learning communities, lesson study, work with instructional coaches, or a partnership with a local college or university, will have a direct influence on the impact of the program. Professional development programs are also more effective when teachers find them to be consistent with other school initiatives and state and national standards. The implementation of CCSSM provides a unique opportunity to focus mathematics teachers' professional development on interpretation and implementation of CCSSM—the standards related to both content and mathematical practice.

- **Opportunities for active learning.** Teachers need to be actively involved in inquiry and problem solving, both with respect to mathematics and pedagogical issues, for professional development to be effective.

Supporting New Teachers

The professional development needs of new teachers are unique. Turnover in the nation's teaching force is high, especially with respect to new teachers and teachers in urban school districts. A significant percentage of new teachers leave the profession within their first five years of service. Beginning teachers are often hired at the last moment, left isolated in their classroom, given the most challenging students and courses to teach, and provided little or no support. The first years of teaching are very challenging and often overwhelming for many novice teachers. Along with professional development and strong professional learning communities within your school, you can help build beginning teachers' confidence and interest in teaching in the following ways:

- Provide new teachers with frequent interactions with master teachers, including the opportunity to observe and be observed by colleagues.

- If instructional math coaches are available, prioritize some of their time to work with and support new teachers.

- Ensure that new teachers become fully functioning and supported members of the most appropriate professional learning community within the school.

- Establish and monitor a mentoring program in your school for new teachers.

- Establish and enforce policies that ensure that new teachers do not inherit the most demanding schedules or the most challenging students.

- Establish and enforce policies that limit new teachers' extracurricular and school-based committee responsibilities.

In addition, NCTM has published two short series of books that are excellent resources for beginning teachers of mathematics and mentors of mathematics teachers. Three "Empowering the Beginning Teacher" books and three "Empowering the Mentor" books offer support in the areas of lesson planning, classroom management, assessment, student motivation, fostering discourse, and professional growth:

Empowering the Beginning Teacher of Mathematics: Elementary School (Chappell, Schielack, and Zagorski 2004)

Empowering the Beginning Teacher of Mathematics: Middle School (Chappell and Pateracki 2004)

Empowering the Beginning Teacher of Mathematics: High School (Chappell, Choppin, and Salls 2004)

Empowering the Mentor of the Beginning Mathematics Teacher (Zimmermann et al. 2009)

Empowering the Mentor of the Experienced Mathematics Teacher (Zimmerman et al. 2009)

Empowering the Mentor of the Preservice Mathematics Teacher (Zimmermann et al. 2009)

Why Family Involvement Is Important

> Parents need to understand that mathematical literacy is just as important as reading literacy.

Forming strong relationships with families is important to a successful mathematics program. Research supports the conclusion that parents' attitudes toward their children's education, and their involvement in it, have a significant impact on classroom success.

Parents can help their children have a good attitude toward mathematics. Adults frequently make comments such as "I can't do math" or "I don't like math." By contrast, a parent is much less likely to say, "I can't read." When a parent—the child's role model—says that he or she does not like or cannot do mathematics, the statement is a signal that the same sentiment is OK on the child's part. Parents need to be educated about how their feelings about mathematics can affect their children's thinking about mathematics and about themselves as mathematicians. They need to understand that mathematical literacy is just as important as reading literacy.

Parents can also serve as advocates for the mathematics program. For parents to do so, they must understand the goals of the mathematics program and the reasons these goals are important. Collaborating with parents and inviting them to participate in efforts to improve the mathematics program are essential for a successful mathematics program for all.

What Information and Resources Should Be Communicated to Families?

The mathematics classroom today may, and most likely should, look very different from the classroom that many parents experienced when they were in school. Some parents may even feel uncomfortable or have misconceptions about the mathematics that their children are learning and the ways in which they are learning it. Therefore, an important role for the administrator and mathematics education leader is to provide parents with information that will help them understand the mathematics program and the ways in which they can contribute to the success of their children's learning (Martin et al. 2011). Some of the steps that administrators can take follow:

- Inform parents of the goals of the mathematics program. Be sure that your discussion includes CCSSM and why CCSSM is important, and share examples that illustrate the standards for content and mathematical practice.

- Provide parents with information on how they can support their children's learning in school and at home.

- Offer hands-on experiences for parents with the curriculum, modeling important mathematical processes and the Standards for Mathematical Practice so that parents can appreciate what and how their children are learning.

- Offer parents hands-on experiences, particularly at the secondary level, with the technology that students use in school, so that parents can see its power and understand that it does not replace thinking by students.

- Communicate to parents the expectation that all students can be successful in mathematics, and share with them the systems that you have developed to monitor students' progress in meeting the expectations of CCSSM and the support programs that you have in place.

- Let parents know that although students are learning in different ways, and conceptual understanding and problem solving receive increased emphasis, the traditional basics and mathematical procedures are still important.

Ways to Communicate with Families

You can communicate effectively with families in a number of ways:

1. Provide information about the mathematics program in newsletters to parents and on the school's website. In particular, discuss CCSSM standards that are currently being addressed in instruction, or each month discuss and define a particular Standard for Mathematical Practice.

2. Host a schoolwide "family math night" in which parents participate in mathematics tasks with their children. This can be effective at both the elementary and secondary levels.

3. Inform parents about the mathematics program during back-to-school nights and parent-teacher conferences. Share the school's grade-level objectives and CCSSM with parents.

4. Encourage parents to volunteer in the mathematics classroom.

Conclusion

Implementation of the Common Core State Standards for Mathematics presents the nation with both new challenges and new opportunities. Although CCSSM presents a vision of mathematics education that is similar to that held by the National Council of Teachers of Mathematics for decades, the unprecedented adoption of the same set of standards by nearly all states in the union provides an opportunity to press "reset" on mathematics education in our nation's schools. Collectively, we have a chance to rededicate ourselves to ensuring that our schools offer effective instruction and have the necessary structures and supports in place to guarantee that all students have the opportunity to acquire the mathematics outlined in CCSSM, continue their education after high school, and become successful and productive members of society. This guide has outlined the process-oriented emphasis on reasoning and sense making that mathematics instruction must have for your students to acquire the standards outlined in CCSSM. In addition, this guide provides specific actions that you can take as an administrator or mathematics education leader in your school to implement the structures and supports needed to improve mathematics education for all students in your school.

The 2003 edition of this guide ended with an excerpt from *Principles and Standards for School Mathematics* (NCTM 2000, pp. 367–68), which effectively summarizes what is needed to ensure a high-quality mathematics education for all students. Implementation of CCSSM makes this summary as relevant today as it was a little more than a decade ago. As a mathematics education leader or administrator, you are uniquely positioned to help make this vision a reality in your school and community:

> Imagine that all mathematics teachers continue to learn new mathematics content and keep current on education research. They collaborate on problems of mathematics teaching and regularly visit one another's classrooms to learn from, and critique, colleagues' teaching. In every school and district, mathematics teacher-leaders are available, serving as expert mentors to their colleagues, recommending resources, orchestrating interaction among teachers, and advising administrators. Education administrators and policymakers at all levels understand the nature of mathematical thinking and learning, help create professional and instructional climates that support students' and teachers' growth, understand the importance of mathematics learning, and provide the time and resources for teachers to teach and students to learn mathematics well. Institutions of higher learning collaborate with schools to study mathematics education and to improve teacher preparation and professional development. Professional mathematicians take an interest in, and contribute constructively to, setting the content goals for mathematics in grades K–12 and for developing teachers' mathematical knowledge. Professional organizations, such as the National Council of Teachers of Mathematics, provide leadership, resources, and professional development opportunities to improve mathematics education. And families, politicians, business and community leaders, and other stakeholders in the system are informed about education issues and serve as valuable resources for schools and children.

Frequently Asked Questions

Q Are the traditional basics still important?

A Absolutely! A major goal in the early grades is the development of computational fluency with whole numbers. Students who lack traditional skills, including knowledge of basic facts—or a way of figuring them out—are at a disadvantage in subsequent mathematics learning (Wallace and Gurganus 2005). The research evidence suggests that students who struggle in mathematics are often those who did not develop fluency with their facts in the elementary grades (Gersten, Jordan, and Flojo 2005). Children need to achieve "fact fluency," but this recall should be based on understanding of the operations and thinking strategies (Fuson 2003; NRC 2001).

Even when students are using calculators or other technology to perform complex calculations, they still need to understand the mathematics. In today's world, students' basic arithmetic skills must include the ability to choose what numbers to use and what operation is appropriate for carrying out the computation, to determine whether the result makes sense, and to decide what to do next. Today, the traditional basics are still necessary, but they are now insufficient. For teachers, by the same token, failure to go beyond teaching basic skills will mean failure to meet the goals of CCSSM and failure to prepare students for the current world of work (Seeley 2009).

Q How should students be grouped?

A Historically, students have often been grouped according to their perceived mathematical abilities. The students in the "higher ability" classes received "high status" mathematics—ideas, concepts, and challenging tasks— whereas students in the "lower ability" classes tended to repeat the same low-level computational skills year after year (Tate and Rousseau 2002). Although some research supports grouping gifted and talented students in homogeneous groups to maximize their learning (Delcourt et al. 1994; Saul, Assouline, and Sheffield 2010), the learning of students assigned to lower-ability groups is depressed, regardless of their ability levels (Stiff, Johnson, and Akos 2011). In addition, once students are placed in low-level or slow math groups, there is a strong probability that they will remain in those low or slow groups until they leave school (Boaler 2008). When students thought to be "at risk" in mathematics are placed in grade-level mathematics courses and provided the support necessary to be successful in those courses, their achievement gains are greater, and they are more likely to enroll in upper-level math courses in the following years, than if they had been placed in lower-ability math courses (Burris, Heubert, and Levin 2006).

Structures that exclude students from a challenging, comprehensive mathematics program based on grade-level CCSSM should be dismantled. It is important to note that some high-performing countries do not separate high achievers from low achievers (particularly in kindergarten–grades 8), do not reduce the number of conceptual techniques in work with lower-achieving students, and do not slow down the pace of instruction with low achievers (Desimore et al. 2005; Education Trust 2005). Students can learn mathematics in heterogeneous groups if structures such as those outlined in this guide are developed to provide appropriate and differentiated support for a range of students.

Q What is the role of practice, drill, and homework in mathematics instruction?

A Practice is important, but not without understanding. Once students understand a computational procedure, practice will help them become confident and develop mastery. However, practice without understanding may be detrimental to students' understanding, and in many cases avoiding this danger means that instruction should place greater emphasis on guided practice—practice that is supported by monitoring and feedback—prior to independent practice (Fuson 2003; NRC 2001). When students mimic a procedure without understanding, they often have difficulty going back later and building understanding (Fuson 2003). Drilling students on facts and procedures without emphasizing understanding also leads students to think that memorization is the key to mathematical proficiency and does not help them understand that mathematics is about thinking and reasoning, as emphasized in the NCTM Process Standards and CCSSM Standards for Mathematical Practice. Students need more than just massed practice. Distributed practice over time with feedback promotes student retention and transfer of knowledge (Pashler et al. 2007).

The research evidence indicates that homework can be effective in improving students' achievement on school-based assessments. In a recent summary of the research, Cooper (2008) found a positive relationship between the amount of homework that students do and their achievement. Short practice assignments were most effective in the elementary grades, up to 90 minutes of homework were most effective in the middle grades, and up to two hours were most effective in high school. Another finding from the research is that homework is most effective when teachers provide reactions to students' homework on a daily basis and give students written descriptive feedback that goes beyond simply marking their work as correct or incorrect (Davies 2007; Marzano 2006; Shuhua 2004).

Q What are the appropriate uses of manipulatives in the mathematics classroom?

A Mathematics achievement in all grades is enhanced through concrete instructional materials and active engagement. Thoughtful, effective use of manipulatives supports CCSSM Standard for Mathematical Practice 5: "Use appropriate tools strategically" (CCSSI 2010, p. 7). Manipulatives are physical objects, such as base-ten blocks, algebra tiles, and geometric solids, and they can make abstract ideas and symbols more meaningful and understandable to students. However, by themselves, manipulatives do not result in learning (Roberts 2007). Students will not automatically make connections between manipulatives and the concepts that they are exploring, and teachers need to help students make the connections (Fuson and Murata 2007). Manipulatives, like technology and other mathematical tools, should support students' conceptual understanding. To ensure that these tools are being used to enhance learning, teachers should help students see connections between them and the mathematical concepts (NRC 2001). Teachers should also systematically help students transfer the understanding that they have gained from using manipulatives to graphical representations and finally to abstract symbols (Witzel, Mercer, and Miller 2003).

Q Will calculators and other technology hurt students' computational skills?

A Using technology does not mean abandoning pencil-and-paper, mental, and other computational strategies. It means that students learn to use technology in appropriate settings and know when using technology makes sense. Studies synthesizing and comparing research over the last two decades support the fact that calculator and computer technologies can enhance student learning. The use of calculators does not harm the development of basic skills and in fact can improve conceptual understanding, problem-solving competence, and higher-level abilities if the technology is purposefully integrated into teaching to supplement and support the development of deep mathematical understanding (Battista 2010; Heid and Blume 2008; Hembree and Dessart 1992; McKenzie Group 2001; NRC 2001; Zbiek 2010).

Q Should elementary schools use mathematics specialists?

A In an effort to improve instruction and learning, some elementary schools are using a model in which designated teachers assume responsibility for teaching mathematics to particular groups of students. Compelling arguments have been made in favor of elementary mathematics teaching specialists (Reys and

Febbell 2003). McGatha (2009) reviewed the literature on elementary mathematics teaching specialists. The limited research to date indicates that the use of mathematics specialists in elementary schools allows those teachers more time to plan math lessons effectively and focus their professional development time. Such a model may be critical to support implementation of CCSSM, which requires teachers to teach in very different ways. Recent research indicates that mathematics teaching specialists may have a greater impact on students' achievement at the intermediate grades and that the positive effect of being taught by a mathematics specialist may be cumulative over two or three years (Campbell 2011).

Q Should schools invest in mathematics instructional coaches?

A Despite the increasing use of mathematics instructional coaches in schools across the country, research on the effectiveness of this approach to professional development is only now emerging (NMAP 2008). According to McGatha (2009), the available empirical and anecdotal evidence indicates that instructional coaching is a promising professional development practice and can be effective in improving teaching and student learning. Recent research suggests that at the intermediate elementary level, math instructional coaches can have a positive effect on student achievement, but it can take up to three years for this effect to emerge, since coaches need time to build constructive relationships with the teachers and administrators with whom they work (Campbell and Malkus 2011). The following sources offer additional guidance on implementing mathematics instructional coaches:

- *A Guide to Mathematics Coaching: Processes for Increasing Student Achievement* (Hull, Balka, and Miles 2009)
- *Instructional Coaching: A Partnership Approach to Improving Instruction* (Knight 2007)
- *Coaching: Approaches and Perspectives* (Knight 2009)

Q Where can research be found to support effective mathematics instruction?

A Increasingly, education leaders look to research when making educational decisions. It is important to understand what research can and cannot do. As Hiebert (1999) and Marzano (2007) have discussed, teaching takes place in a complex environment, and research does not provide definitive answers to questions. Instead, recommendations based on research rest on probability estimates—that is, what is likely to improve student learning—and recommendations will change over time as new information emerges. Despite these limitations, we do know a good deal from the research about effective mathematics teaching and learning (Reed 2008). This guide cites relevant research whenever possible. In addition, one of NCTM's strategic initiatives in the last half-decade has been to link research and practice. As part of this initiative, NCTM has published a number of resources that you can consult to find additional research to improve teaching and learning:

- *Disrupting Tradition: Research and Practice Pathways in Mathematics Education* (Tate, King, and Anderson 2011)

- *Teaching and Learning Mathematics: Translating Research for Secondary School Teachers* (Lobato and Lester 2010)

- *Teaching and Learning Mathematics: Translating Research for Elementary School Teachers* (Lambdin and Lester 2010)

- *Teaching and Learning Mathematics: Translating Research for School Administrators* (Charles and Lester 2010)

- *Second Handbook of Research on Mathematics Teaching and Learning* (Lester 2007)

- *A Research Companion to "Principles and Standards for School Mathematics"* (Kilpatrick, Martin, and Schifter 2003)

- NCTM's Research Briefs and Clips, available at www.nctm.org/researchbriefs.aspx

Q How can ELL students be supported in learning mathematics?

A It should not be assumed that ELL students will struggle in mathematics. With appropriate instruction and support, ELL students can be successful in meeting the benchmarks outlined in CCSSM. ELL students need access to the same rigorous mathematics courses that other students have access to, and they should not be denied opportunities to engage in reasoning activities (Civil 2011; Coggins 2007; Moschkovich 2007). Teachers frequently limit discourse interactions with ELL students during mathematics instruction. The research, however, indicates that literacy-rich classrooms actually support ELL students' development of both academic language proficiency and mathematics content knowledge (Bay-Williams and Herrera 2007). To facilitate this progress, ELL students need direct vocabulary instruction. Effective instruction to support ELL students must not treat mathematics vocabulary as isolated terms but instead locate it within the context of situations in which understanding can be developed. Such instruction uses a variety of visual tools, promotes group interactions, uses multiple representations, and provides specific language supports—for example, modeling think-aloud strategies during instruction (Bay-Williams and Herrera, 2007; Coggins 2007). Characteristics of teachers who have succeeded in teaching ELL students include (*a*) high commitment to students' success, (*b*) high expectations for all students, (*c*) autonomy to change curriculum and instruction to meet individual needs, (*d*) a view of students as intellectually capable (Moschkovich 2011).

Q What are effective strategies for teaching students with difficulties in mathematics?

A In general, students with difficulties in mathematics should receive instruction that emphasizes all aspects of mathematical proficiency, with the same teaching and the learning principles applying to all students, including those with special needs (Baroody 2011). In a recent summary of the research on specific instructional strategies that have consistently been found to be effective in teaching students who experience difficulties with mathematics, Gersten and Clarke (2007, p. 2) reached the following conclusions:

> For low-achieving students, the use of structured peer-assisted learning activities, along with systematic and explicit instruction and formative data furnished both to the teacher and to students, appears to be most important. For special education students, explicit, systematic instruction that involves extensive use of visual representations appears to be crucial. In many situations with special education students, it is often advantageous for students to be encouraged to think aloud while they work, perhaps by sharing their thinking with a peer. These approaches also seem to inhibit those students who try too quickly and impulsively to solve problems without devoting adequate attention to thinking about what mathematical concepts and principles are required for the solution. Instruction should ideally be in a small group of no more than six and (*a*) address skills that are necessary for the unit at hand, (*b*) be quite explicit and systematic, and (*c*) require the student to think aloud as she or he solves problems or uses graphic representation to work through problem-solving options. Finally, it should balance work on basic whole-number or rational-number operations (depending on grade level) with strategies for solving problems that are more complex. These criteria should be considered in evaluating intervention programs for working with these types of students.

Another recent review of the research on instruction for students with learning disabilities in mathematics has similarly found that a systematic and explicit approach to instruction is most effective (Gersten et al. 2009b). This approach is characterized by teacher modeling, followed by students' practicing with similar problems and receiving specific and immediate feedback from the teacher as they verbalize and explain their solutions and understandings, followed by ongoing cumulative review of key concepts (Clarke et al. 2011).

NCTM recently published a useful resource, *Achieving Fluency: Special Education and Mathematics* (Fennell 2011), which offers teachers and leaders additional specific strategies to support learners who struggle with mathematics.

Q What should be used for mathematics intervention, or RtI?

A RtI is more accurately viewed as a process of response to students' needs than as a program or product. As Baroody (2011) has asserted, "The major source of most mathematical learning difficulties is how children are taught (psychologically inappropriate instruction), not their mental equipment (organic or cognitive dysfunction)" (p. 30). Therefore, the most important tier in the three-tier RtI model is Tier 1—highly effective classroom instruction, as outlined in this guide. The report of the National Mathematics Advisory Panel recommended that a component of Tier 1 instruction be the use of formative assessment to provide targeted *additional* instruction and support as the next level in a tiered response to meet students' needs (NMAP 2008). Successful interventions address students' conceptual understanding and problem-solving abilities in addition to their procedural fluency. Such interventions address not only targeted re-teaching needs but also students' prior misconceptions, which may underlie their current difficulties. A key is that RtI support must be provided *in addition to* having students remain in the regular classroom. The practice of removing students from math class to receive intervention support results only in their falling further behind as they miss out on grade-level instruction.

Before implementing supplementary programs for intervention, school leaders should carefully analyze whether or not teachers have implemented the type of formative assessment system linked to additional instructional support, as well as the instructional strategies known to be effective with students who experience difficulties in mathematics, as outlined in this guide for Tier 1 instruction. If highly effective Tier 1 instructional practices and structures are in place, the number of students who need Tier 2 or Tier 3 instruction or supplementary programs may be substantially reduced. Research indicates that with effective Tier 1 instruction, approximately 80 percent of students' mathematics learning difficulties can be prevented (Gersten et al. 2009a; Wixson 2011).

Q What are effective strategies to motivate students to learn mathematics?

A Often, teachers believe that students are either motivated or not and that teachers have little control over students' motivation. The research, however, indicates that teachers can build students' interest, confidence, and motivation in mathematics (Middleton and Jansen 2011; Turner, Warzon, and Christensen 2011). Middleton and Jansen (2011) outline six principles of motivation:

1. Motivation is learned.

2. Motivation is adaptive.

3. Motivation is "in the moment."

4. Motivation creates long-term attitudes.

5. Motivation is social.

6. Success matters.

In addition, they outline five categories of instructional strategies that teachers can implement to build student motivation and engagement:

1. Using contexts judiciously

2. Providing challenge

3. Limiting the use of rewards and other reinforcers

4. Exploiting interests

5. Building relationships

Details regarding Middleton and Jansen's principles of motivation and instructional strategies can be found in their book, *Motivation Matters and Interest Counts: Fostering Engagement in Mathematics* (2011). An additional resource on motivation is the 2011 NCTM Yearbook, *Motivation and Disposition: Pathways to Learning Mathematics* (Brahier 2011).

Additional Resources

NCTM's underlying philosophy and its foundational publications offer administrators, mathematics education leaders, and teachers support in interpreting and implementing the Common Core State Standards for Mathematics. Administrators can point teachers to and encourage them to use the Council's continually growing collection of resources to flesh out CCSSM and fully engage students in doing mathematics. The extensive collection of materials that NCTM has developed to support and demonstrate the Council's Standards can similarly inform interpretation and implementation of CCSSM.

NCTM can also help fill in some gaps in CCSSM. For example, NCTM's prekindergarten materials provide guidance for parents and early childhood educators in preparing young children to get the most out of their kindergarten mathematics experiences. NCTM's resources can help ensure that the full vision of CCSSM is achieved.

CCSSM Resources

- *Making It Happen: A Guide to Interpreting and Implementing Common Core State Standards for Mathematics* (NCTM 2010)
- Common Core State Standards Initiative: www.corestandards.org
- Partnership for the Assessment of Readiness for College and Careers (PARCC): http://www.parcconline.org
- Smarter Balanced Assessment Consortium (SBAC): www.k12.wa.us/smarter/

Leadership Resources

- *A Guide to Mathematics Leadership: Sequencing Instructional Change* (Balka, Hull, and Miles 2009)
- *The PRIME Leadership Framework* (National Council of Supervisors of Mathematics 2008)
- National Council of Supervisors of Mathematics: www.ncsmonline.org

High School Reasoning and Sense Making Resources

- *Focus in High School Mathematics: Reasoning and Sense Making* (NCTM 2009)

- *Focus in High School Mathematics: Fostering Reasoning and Sense Making for All Students* (Strutchens and Quander 2011)

- *Focus in High School Mathematics: Reasoning and Sense Making in Algebra* (Graham, Cuoco, and Zimmermann 2010)

- *Focus in High School Mathematics: Reasoning and Sense Making in Geometry* (McCrone et al. 2010)

- *Focus in High School Mathematics: Reasoning and Sense Making in Statistics and Probability* (Shaughnessy, Chance, and Kranendonk 2009)

- *Focus in High School Mathematics: Technology to Support Reasoning and Sense Making* (Dick and Hollebrands 2011)

Curriculum Resources

- *Curriculum Focal Points for Teaching Mathematics in Prekindergarten through Grade 8: A Quest for Coherence* (*NCTM* 2006).

- Teaching with Curriculum Focal Points series. This NCTM series supplements *Curriculum Focal Points* with detailed guidance on instructional progressions, ways to introduce topics, and suggestions to build deeper understanding of essential topics. The series includes grade-level volumes for pre-K–grade 8 and grade-band volumes for pre-K–grade 2, grades 3–5, and grades 6–8.

- *Principles and Standards for School Mathematics* (NCTM 2000).

- *Principles and Standards for School Mathematics* Navigations Series. This NCTM series features hands-on student activities to support teachers in implementing ideas consistent with *Principles and Standards.* The series consists of thirty-five volumes, with grade-band books in each of the major mathematics content areas, as well as books covering the mathematical processes (problem solving, reasoning and proof, communication, connections, and representation) and two volumes on discrete mathematics.

Diversity, Intervention, and Differentiation Resources

- *Mathematics for Every Student: Responding to Diversity, Grades Pre-K–5* (White, Spitzer, and Malloy 2009)
- *Mathematics for Every Student: Responding to Diversity, Grades 6–8* (Ellis and Malloy 2009)
- *Mathematics for Every Student: Responding to Diversity, Grades 9–12* (Flores and Malloy 2009)
- *Models of Intervention in Mathematics: Reweaving the Tapestry* (Fosnot 2010)
- *The Peak in the Middle: Developing Mathematically Gifted Students in the Middle Grades* (Saul, Assouline, and Sheffield 2010)
- *Good Questions: Great Ways to Differentiate Mathematics Instruction* (Small 2009)
- *More Good Questions: Great Ways to Differentiate Secondary Mathematics Instruction* (Small and Lin 2010)

Professional Development Resources

- *Designing Professional Development for Teachers of Science and Mathematics* (3rd ed.) (Loucks-Horsley et al. 2009)
- *Growing Professionally* (Bay-Williams and Karp 2008)
- Essential Understanding Series. This sixteen-book NCTM series addresses topics in pre-K–12 mathematics that are often difficult to teach but critical to student development. Each book gives an overview of the topic, highlights the differences between what students and teachers need to know, examines the "big ideas" and related essential understandings, reconsiders the ideas presented in light of connections with other ideas, and includes questions for reflection.

Mathematical Discourse Resources

- *5 Practices for Orchestrating Productive Mathematics Discussions* (Smith and Stein 2011)
- *Promoting Purposeful Discourse: Teacher Research in Mathematics Classrooms* (Herbel-Eisenmann and Cirillo 2009)
- *Getting into the Mathematics Conversation: Valuing Communication in Mathematics Classrooms* (Elliott and Garnett 2008)

Early Childhood Resources

- *The Young Child and Mathematics* (2nd ed.) (Copley 2010)
- *Young Mathematicians at Work: Constructing Algebra* (Fosnot and Jacob 2010)
- *Mathematics Learning in Early Childhood: Paths toward Excellence and Equity* (NRC 2009)

Appendix A

Interpretation Charts for Prekindergarten–Grade 8

Interpreting CCSSM for Prekindergarten

CCSSM Critical Area (CCSSM does not include standards for prekindergarten.)	*Principles and Standards* For information about instructional goals related to the mathematics content in this critical area	*Curriculum Focal Points* For information about how this content appears within an example of a focused curriculum proposed by NCTM	Essential Understanding Series For an articulation of mathematical understanding that is essential for teachers working in this critical area
	See Pre-K–Grade 2 Number and Operations— Understand numbers, ways of representing numbers, relationships among numbers, and number systems (pp. 79–83), *regarding the expectation that students—* • connect number words and numerals to the quantities they represent, using various physical models and representations. *See* Pre-K–Grade 2 Algebra— Analyze change in various contexts (p. 95), *regarding the expectation that students—* • describe qualitative change, such as a student's growing taller.	*For an example of the placement of developing understanding of whole numbers in a focused curriculum, see* Prekindergarten Focal Point for Number and Operations: Developing an understanding of whole numbers, including concepts of correspondence, counting, cardinality, and comparison (p. 11).	*See* Pre-K–Grade 2 Number and Numeration *for an essential understanding of—* • the relationship between physical objects, their attributes, and quantity (pp. 11–14); • the importance of choosing a unit when using numbers to compare quantities such as two heights (pp. 19–26).
	See Pre-K–Grade 2 Geometry— Specify locations and describe spatial relationships using coordinate geometry and other representational systems (pp. 98–99), *regarding the expectation that students—* • describe, name, and interpret relative positions in space and apply ideas about relative position; • find and name locations with simple relationships such as "near to".... *See* Pre-K–Grade 2 Geometry— Use visualization, spatial reasoning, and geometric modeling to solve problems (pp. 100–101), *regarding the expectation that students—* • recognize geometric shapes and structures in the environment and specify their location.	*For an example of the placement of developing understanding of shapes and space, see* Prekindergarten Focal Point for Geometry: Identifying shapes and describing spatial relationships (p. 11).	**Projected:** *See* Pre-K–Grade 2 Geometry (anticipated 2012) *for underlying ideas about—* • shapes and space.

Interpreting CCSSM for Kindergarten

CCSSM Critical Area	*Principles and Standards* For information about instructional goals related to the mathematics content in this critical area	*Curriculum Focal Points* For information about how this content appears within an example of a focused curriculum proposed by NCTM	Essential Understanding Series For an articulation of mathematical understanding that is essential for teachers working in this critical area
(1) Representing, relating, and operating on whole numbers, initially with sets of objects	*See* Pre-K–Grade 2 Number and Operations— Understand numbers, ways of representing numbers, relationships among numbers, and number systems (pp. 79–83), *regarding the expectation that students—* • develop a sense of whole numbers and represent and use them in flexible ways, including relating, composing, and decomposing numbers; • connect number words and numerals to the quantities they represent, using various physical models and representations. *See* Pre-K–Grade 2 Number and Operations— Understand meanings of operations and how they relate to one another (pp. 83–84), *regarding the expectation that students—* • understand various meanings of addition and subtraction of whole numbers and the relationship between the two operations; • understand the effects of adding and subtracting whole numbers. *See* Pre-K–Grade 2 Algebra— Use mathematical models to represent and understand quantitative relationships (p. 95), *regarding the expectation that students—* • model situations that involve the addition and subtraction of whole numbers, using objects, pictures, and symbols. *See* Pre-K–Grade 2 Algebra—Analyze change in various contexts (p. 95), *regarding the expectation that students—* • describe qualitative change, such as a student's growing taller; • describe quantitative change, such as a student's growing two inches in one year.	*For an example of the placement of developing understanding of whole numbers in a focused curriculum, see* Kindergarten Focal Point for Number and Operations: Representing, comparing, and ordering whole numbers and joining and separating sets (p. 12).	*See* Pre-K–Grade 2 Number and Numeration *for an essential understanding of—* • the fundamental relationship among objects, their attributes, and counting (pp. 10–18); • strategies and uses for composing and decomposing whole numbers in terms of part-whole relationships (pp. 25–26); • number as an abstract concept and the relationship of number to the number-word sequence (pp. 32–34); • the connection of counting strategies and decomposition to addition and subtraction (pp. 43–45). *See* Pre-K–Grade 2 Addition and Subtraction *for an essential understanding of—* • addition and subtraction of whole numbers based on sequential counting of objects; • addition and subtraction in terms of part-whole relationships with sets of objects.

Interpreting CCSSM for Kindergarten—*Continued*

CCSSM Critical Area	Principles and Standards For information about instructional goals related to the mathematics content in this critical area	Curriculum Focal Points For information about how this content appears within an example of a focused curriculum proposed by NCTM	Essential Understanding Series For an articulation of mathematical understanding that is essential for teachers working in this critical area
(2) Describing shapes and space	*See* Pre-K–Grade 2 Geometry— Analyze characteristics and properties of two- and three-dimensional geometric shapes and develop mathematical arguments about geometric relationships (pp. 97–98), *regarding the expectation that students—* • recognize, name, build, draw, compare, and sort two- and three-dimensional shapes. *See* Pre-K–Grade 2 Geometry— Specify locations and describe spatial relationships using coordinate geometry and other representational systems (pp. 98–99), *regarding the expectation that students—* • describe, name, and interpret relative positions in space and apply ideas about relative position; • find and name locations with simple relationships such as "near to"…. *See* Pre-K–Grade 2 Geometry— Use visualization, spatial reasoning, and geometric modeling to solve problems (pp. 100–101), *regarding the expectation that students—* • recognize geometric shapes and structures in the environment and specify their location.	*For an example of the placement of developing understanding of base-ten numeration value in a focused curriculum, see* Kindergarten Focal Point for Geometry: Describing shapes and space (p. 12).	Projected: *See* Pre-K–Grade 2 Geometry (anticipated 2012) *for underlying ideas about—* • shapes and space.

Interpreting CCSSM for Grade 1

CCSSM Critical Area	Principles and Standards For information about instructional goals related to the mathematics content in this critical area	Curriculum Focal Points For information about how this content appears within an example of a focused curriculum proposed by NCTM	Essential Understanding Series For an articulation of mathematical understanding that is essential for teachers working in this critical area
(1) Developing understanding of addition, subtraction, and strategies for addition and subtraction within 20	*See* Pre-K–Grade 2 Number and Operations—Understand meanings of operations and how they relate to one another (pp. 83–84), *regarding the expectation that students—* • understand various meanings of addition and subtraction of whole numbers and the relationship between the two operations; • understand the effects of adding and subtracting whole numbers. *See* Pre-K–Grade 2 Number and Operations—Compute fluently and make reasonable estimates (pp. 84–88), *regarding the expectation that students—* • develop and use strategies for whole number computations, with a focus on addition and subtraction. *See* Pre-K–Grade 2 Algebra—Represent and analyze mathematical situations and structures using algebraic symbols (p. 93–95), *regarding the expectation that students—* • illustrate general principles and properties of operations, such as commutativity, using specific numbers; • use concrete, pictorial, and verbal representations to develop an understanding of invented and conventional symbolic notations. *See* Pre-K–Grade 2 Algebra—Use mathematical models to represent and understand quantitative relationships (p. 95), *regarding the expectation that students—* • model situations that involve the addition and subtraction of whole numbers, using objects, pictures, and symbols. *See* Pre-K–Grade 2 Algebra—Analyze change in various contexts (p. 95), *regarding the expectation that students—* • describe quantitative change, such as a student's growing two inches in one year.	*For an example of the placement of developing fluency with addition and subtraction of whole numbers in a focused curriculum,* see Grade 1 Focal Point for Number and Operations and Algebra: Developing understandings of addition and subtraction and strategies for basic addition facts and related subtraction facts (p. 13).	*See* Pre-K–Grade 2 Addition and Subtraction *for an essential understanding of—* • the identification of different problem situations that can be represented by part-part-whole relationships and addition or subtraction and strategies appropriate for these situations; • the structure of word problems and the structure of expressions; • the use of appropriate language in addition and subtraction contexts; • the use of student-invented strategies.

Interpreting the Common Core State Standards to Improve Mathematics Education

CCSSM Critical Area	*Principles and Standards* For information about instructional goals related to the mathematics content in this critical area	*Curriculum Focal Points* For information about how this content appears within an example of a focused curriculum proposed by NCTM	Essential Understanding Series For an articulation of mathematical understanding that is essential for teachers working in this critical area
(2) Developing understanding of whole number relationships and place value, including grouping in tens and ones	*See* Pre-K–Grade 2 Number and Operations—Understand numbers, ways of representing numbers, relationships among numbers, and number systems (pp. 79–83), *regarding the expectation that students—* • use multiple models to develop initial understandings of place value and the base-ten number system; • develop a sense of whole numbers and represent and use them in flexible ways, including relating, composing, and decomposing numbers; • connect number words and numerals to the quantities they represent, using various physical models and representations.	*For an example of the placement of developing understanding of base-ten numeration value in a focused curriculum, see* Grade 1 Focal Point for Number and Operations: Developing an understanding of whole number relationships, including grouping in tens and ones (p. 13).	*See* Pre-K–Grade 2 Number and Numeration *for an essential understanding of—* • explicit and implicit characteristics of the base-ten number system, including how an understanding of unit in counting facilitates grouping with place-value units (pp. 35–41). See Pre-K–Grade 2 Addition and Subtraction *for an essential understanding of—* • place-value concepts as a convenient way to compose and decompose numbers to facilitate addition and subtraction computations.

CCSSM Critical Area	*Principles and Standards* For information about instructional goals related to the mathematics content in this critical area	*Curriculum Focal Points* For information about how this content appears within an example of a focused curriculum proposed by NCTM	Essential Understanding Series For an articulation of mathematical understanding that is essential for teachers working in this critical area
(3) Developing understanding of linear measurement and measuring lengths as iterating length units	*See* Pre-K–Grade 2 Measurement— Understand measurable attributes of objects and the units, systems, and processes of measurement (pp. 103–5), *regarding the expectation that students*— • understand how to measure using nonstandard and standard units; • select an appropriate unit and tool for the attribute being measured. *See* Pre-K–Grade 2 Measurement— Apply appropriate techniques, tools, and formulas to determine measurements (pp. 105–6), *regarding the expectation that students*— • measure with multiple copies of units of the same size, such as paper clips laid end to end; • use repetition of a single unit to measure something larger than the unit, for instance, measuring the length of a room with a single meter stick; • use tools to measure; • develop common referents for measures to make comparisons and estimates.	*For an example of the placement of developing an understanding of measurement in a focused curriculum, see* Kindergarten Focal Point for Measurement: Ordering objects by measurable attributes (p. 12). *For an example of the placement of developing an understanding of linear measurement in a focused curriculum, see* Grade 2 Focal Point for Measurement: Developing an understanding of linear measurement and facility in measuring lengths (p. 14).	*See* Pre-K–Grade 2 Number and Numeration *for an essential understanding of*— • the nontrivial relationship among an object and its attributes and measures (pp. 11–14); • the centrality of unit in measuring and comparing quantities (pp. 19–26); • ways of developing ideas about length by building on counting and number line models to foreshadow rational numbers (pp. 46–49).
(4) Reasoning about attributes of, and composing and decomposing, geometric shapes.	*See* Pre-K–Grade 2 Geometry— Analyze characteristics and properties of two- and three-dimensional geometric shapes and develop mathematical arguments about geometric relationships (pp. 97–98), *regarding the expectation that students*— • recognize, name, build, draw, compare, and sort two- and three-dimensional shapes; • describe attributes and parts of two- and three-dimensional shapes; • investigate and predict the results of putting together and taking apart two- and three-dimensional shapes.	*For an example of the placement of developing an understanding of describing and analyzing shapes in a focused curriculum, see* Grade 1 Focal Point for Geometry: Composing and decomposing geometric shapes (p. 13).	**Projected:** *See* Pre-K–Grade 2 Geometry (anticipated 2012) for underlying ideas about— • shapes.

Interpreting CCSSM for Grade 2

CCSSM Critical Area	*Principles and Standards* For information about instructional goals related to the mathematics content in this critical area	*Curriculum Focal Points* For information about how this content appears within an example of a focused curriculum proposed by NCTM	*Essential Understanding Series* For an articulation of mathematical understanding that is essential for teachers working in this critical area
(1) Extending understanding of base-ten notation	*See* Pre-K–Grade 2 Number and Operations— Understand numbers, ways of representing numbers, relationships among numbers, and number systems (pp. 79–83), *regarding the expectation that students—* • use multiple models to develop initial understandings of place value and the base-ten number system; • develop a sense of whole numbers and represent and use them in flexible ways, including relating, composing, and decomposing numbers; • connect number words and numerals to the quantities they represent, using various physical models and representations.	*For an example of the placement of developing understanding of base-ten numeration value in a focused curriculum, see* Grade 2 Focal Point for Number and Operations: Developing an understanding of the base-ten numeration system and place-value concepts (p. 14).	*See* Pre-K–Grade 2 Number and Numeration *for an essential understanding of—* • the nontrivial relationship among an object and its attributes and measures (pp. 11–14); • explicit and implicit characteristics of the base-ten number system, including how an understanding of unit in counting facilitates grouping with place-value units (pp. 35–41).
(2) Building fluency with addition and subtraction	*See* Pre-K–Grade 2 Number and Operations— Understand meanings of operations and how they relate to one another (pp. 83–84), *regarding the expectation that students—* • understand various meanings of addition and subtraction of whole numbers and the relationship between the two operations; • understand the effects of adding and subtracting whole numbers. *See* Pre-K–Grade 2 Number and Operations— Compute fluently and make reasonable estimates (pp. 84–88), *regarding the expectation that students—* • develop and use strategies for whole number computations, with a focus on addition and subtraction; • develop fluency with basic number combinations for addition and subtraction; • use a variety of methods and tools to compute, including objects, mental computation, estimation, paper and pencil, and calculators.	*For an example of the placement of developing fluency with addition and subtraction of whole numbers in a focused curriculum, see* Grade 2 Focal Point for Number and Operations and Algebra: Developing quick recall of addition facts and related subtraction facts and fluency with multi-digit addition and subtraction (p. 14).	*See* Pre-K–Grade 2 Addition and Subtraction *for an essential understanding of—* • commutative and associative properties for addition of whole numbers as tools that allow computations to be performed flexibly; • structure of word problems and structure of expressions; • appropriate language in addition and subtraction contexts; • use of student-invented strategies; • place-value concepts as a convenient way to compose and decompose numbers to facilitate addition and subtraction computations; • comparative difficulty of addition and subtraction.

Interpreting CCSSM for Grade 2—*Continued*

CCSSM Critical Area	*Principles and Standards* For information about instructional goals related to the mathematics content in this critical area	*Curriculum Focal Points* For information about how this content appears within an example of a focused curriculum proposed by NCTM	Essential Understanding Series For an articulation of mathematical understanding that is essential for teachers working in this critical area
(2) Building fluency with addition and subtraction	*See* Pre-K–Grade 2 Algebra— Use mathematical models to represent and understand quantitative relationships (p. 95), *regarding the expectation that students—* • model situations that involve the addition and subtraction of whole numbers, using objects, pictures, and symbols. *See* Pre-K–Grade 2 Algebra— Analyze change in various contexts (p. 95), *regarding the expectation that students—* • describe quantitative change, such as a student's growing two inches in one year.		
(3) Using standard units of measure	*See* Pre-K–Grade 2 Measurement— Understand measurable attributes of objects and the units, systems, and processes of measurement (pp. 103–105), *regarding the expectation that students—* • understand how to measure using nonstandard and standard units; • select an appropriate unit and tool for the attribute being measured. *See* Pre-K–Grade 2 Measurement— Apply appropriate techniques, tools, and formulas to determine measurements (pp. 105–106), *regarding the expectation that students—* • measure with multiple copies of units of the same size, such as paper clips laid end to end; • use repetition of a single unit to measure something larger than the unit, for instance, measuring the length of a room with a single meter stick; • use tools to measure; • develop common referents for measures to make comparisons and estimates.	*For an example of the placement of developing an understanding of linear measurement in a focused curriculum, see* Grade 2 Focal Point for Measurement: Developing an understanding of linear measurement and facility in measuring lengths (p. 14).	*See* Pre-K–Grade 2 Number and Numeration *for an essential understanding of—* • the centrality of unit in measuring and comparing quantities (pp. 19–26). *See* Grades 3–5 Rational Numbers *for an essential understanding of—* • the fundamental concept of unit in the interpretation of rational numbers (pp. 19–20); • interpretations of rational numbers as measures (pp. 21–23); • connections between measurement and rational number (p. 61).

Interpreting CCSSM for Grade 2—*Continued*

CCSSM Critical Area	*Principles and Standards* For information about instructional goals related to the mathematics content in this critical area	*Curriculum Focal Points* For information about how this content appears within an example of a focused curriculum proposed by NCTM	**Essential Understanding Series** For an articulation of mathematical understanding that is essential for teachers working in this critical area
(4) Describing and analyzing shapes	*See* Grades 3–5 Geometry— Analyze characteristics and properties of two- and three-dimensional geometric shapes and develop mathematical arguments about geometric relationships (pp. 165–66), *regarding the expectation that students*— • identify, compare, and analyze attributes of two- and three-dimensional shapes and develop vocabulary to describe the attributes; • classify two- and three-dimensional shapes according to their properties and develop definitions of classes of shapes such as triangles and pyramids.	*For an example of the placement of developing an understanding of describing and analyzing shapes in a focused curriculum, see* Grade 3 Focal Point for Geometry: Describing and analyzing properties of two-dimensional shapes (p. 15).	**Projected:** *See* Pre-K–Grade 2 Geometry *and* Grades 3–5 Geometry (both anticipated 2012) *for underlying ideas about*— • shapes.

Interpreting CCSSM for Grade 3

CCSSM Critical Area	*Principles and Standards* For information about instructional goals related to the mathematics content in this critical area	*Curriculum Focal Points* For information about how this content appears within an example of a focused curriculum proposed by NCTM	*Essential Understanding Series* For an articulation of mathematical understanding that is essential for teachers working in this critical area
(1) Developing understanding of multiplication and division and strategies for multiplication and division within 100	*See* Grades 3–5 Number and Operations— Understand meanings of operations and how they relate to one another (pp. 151–52), *regarding the expectation that students—* • understand various meanings of multiplication and division; • understand the effects of multiplying and dividing whole numbers; • identify and use relationships between operations, such as division as the inverse of multiplication, to solve problems. *See* Grades 3–5 Number and Operations— Compute fluently and make reasonable estimates (pp. 152–56), *regarding the expectation that students—* • develop fluency with basic number combinations for multiplication and division and use these combinations to mentally compute related problems, such as 30 × 50; • develop fluency in adding, subtracting, multiplying, and dividing whole numbers; • develop and use strategies to estimate the results of whole number computations and to judge the reasonableness of such results. *See* Grades 3–5 Algebra— Represent and analyze mathematical situations and structures using algebraic symbols (pp. 160–62), *regarding the expectation that students—* • identify such properties as commutativity, associativity, and distributivity and use them to compute with whole numbers; • represent the idea of a variable as an unknown quantity using a letter or a symbol; • express mathematical relationships using equations. *See* Grades 3–5 Algebra— Use mathematical models to represent and understand quantitative relationships (pp. 162–63), *regarding the expectation that students—* • model problem situations with objects and use representations such as graphs, tables, and equations to draw conclusions.	*For an example of the placement of developing the meanings of and strategies for multiplication and division in a focused curriculum, see* Grade 3 Focal Point for Number and Operations and Algebra: Developing understandings of multiplication and division and strategies for basic multiplication facts and related division facts (p. 15).	*See* Grades 3–5 Multiplication and Division *for an essential understanding of—* • a scalar view of multiplication; • representing and solving problems beyond whole number multiplication and division with a scalar view of multiplication; • division defined by its inverse relationship with multiplication; • connections of division with topics from prekindergarten–grade 2, including place value, addition, subtraction, and skip counting.

Interpreting CCSSM for Grade 3—*Continued*

CCSSM Critical Area	*Principles and Standards* For information about instructional goals related to the mathematics content in this critical area	*Curriculum Focal Points* For information about how this content appears within an example of a focused curriculum proposed by NCTM	Essential Understanding Series For an articulation of mathematical understanding that is essential for teachers working in this critical area
(2) Developing understanding of fractions, especially unit fractions (fractions with numerator 1)	*See* Grades 3–5 Number and Operations— Understand numbers, ways of representing numbers, relationships among numbers, and number systems (pp. 149–51), *regarding the expectation that students*— • develop understanding of fractions as parts of unit wholes, as parts of a collection, as locations on number lines, and as divisions of whole numbers; • use models, benchmarks, and equivalent forms to judge the size of fractions.	*For an example of the placement of developing understanding of fractions in a focused curriculum,* see Grade 3 Focal Point for Number and Operations: Developing an understanding of fractions and fraction equivalence (p. 15).	*See* Grades 3–5 Rational Numbers *for an essential understanding of—* • an interpretation of rational numbers as part-whole relationships (pp. 20–21); • ordering rational numbers and its relationship to equivalence (pp. 76–78).
(3) Developing understanding of the structure of rectangular arrays and of area	*See* Grades 3–5 Measurement— Understand measurable attributes of objects and the units, systems, and processes of measurement (pp. 172–73), *regarding the expectation that students*— • understand such attributes as length, area, weight, volume, and size of angle and select the appropriate type of unit for measuring each attribute. *See* Grades 3–5 Measurement— Apply appropriate techniques, tools, and formulas to determine measurements (pp. 173–75), *regarding the expectation that students*— • develop strategies for estimating the perimeters, areas, and volumes of irregular shapes; • select and apply appropriate standard units and tools to measure length, area, volume, weight, time, temperature, and the size of angles; • develop, understand, and use formulas to find the area of rectangles and related triangles and parallelograms.	*For an example of the placement of rectangular arrays and area and their connection to multiplication in a focused curriculum,* see Grade 3 Focal Point for Number and Operations and Algebra: Developing understandings of multiplication and division and strategies for basic multiplication facts and related division facts (p. 15); *and* Grade 4 Focal Point for Measurement: Developing an understanding of area and determining the areas of two-dimensional shapes (p. 16).	*See* Grades 3–5 Multiplication and Division *for an essential understanding of—* • rectangular arrays and area models as representations of multiplication; • working with an area model of multiplication.

CCSSM Critical Area	*Principles and Standards* For information about instructional goals related to the mathematics content in this critical area	*Curriculum Focal Points* For information about how this content appears within an example of a focused curriculum proposed by NCTM	Essential Understanding Series For an articulation of mathematical understanding that is essential for teachers working in this critical area
(4) Describing and analyzing two-dimensional shapes	*See* Grades 3–5 Geometry— Analyze characteristics and properties of two- and three-dimensional geometric shapes and develop mathematical arguments about geometric relationships (pp. 165–67), *regarding the expectation that students—* • identify, compare, and analyze attributes of two- and three-dimensional shapes and develop vocabulary to describe the attributes; • classify two- and three-dimensional shapes according to their properties and develop definitions of classes of shapes such as triangles and pyramids; • investigate, describe, and reason about the results of subdividing, combining, and transforming shapes.	*For an example of the placement of content related to describing and analyzing two-dimensional shapes, see* Grade 3 Focal Point for Geometry: Describing and analyzing properties of two-dimensional shapes (p. 15).	**Projected:** *See* Grades 3–5 Geometry (anticipated 2012) *for underlying ideas about—* • two-dimensional shapes.

Interpreting CCSSM for Grade 4

CCSSM Critical Area	Principles and Standards For information about instructional goals related to the mathematics content in this critical area	Curriculum Focal Points For information about how this content appears within an example of a focused curriculum proposed by NCTM	Essential Understanding Series For an articulation of mathematical understanding that is essential for teachers working in this critical area
(1) Developing understanding and fluency with multi-digit multiplication, and developing understanding of dividing to find quotients involving multi-digit dividends	*See* Grades 3–5 Number and Operations— Understand numbers, ways of representing numbers, relationships among numbers, and number systems (pp. 149–51), *regarding the expectation that students*— • understand the place-value structure of the base-ten number system.... *See* Grades 3–5 Number and Operations— Understand meanings of operations and how they relate to one another (pp. 151–52), *regarding the expectation that students*— • understand various meanings of multiplication and division; • understand the effects of multiplying and dividing whole numbers; • identify and use relationships between operations, such as division as the inverse of multiplication, to solve problems; • understand and use properties of operations, such as the distributivity of multiplication over addition. *See* Grades 3–5 Number and Operations— Compute fluently and make reasonable estimates (pp. 152–56), *regarding the expectation that students*— • develop fluency with basic number combinations for multiplication and division and use these combinations to mentally compute related problems, such as 30×50; • develop fluency in adding, subtracting, multiplying, and dividing whole numbers; • develop and use strategies to estimate the results of whole number computations and to judge the reasonableness of such results; • select appropriate methods and tools for computing with whole numbers from among mental computation, estimation, calculators, and paper and pencil according to the context and nature of the computation and use the selected method or tool.	*For an example of the placement of developing fluency with multiplication and division in a focused curriculum, see* Grade 4 Focal Point for Number and Operations and Algebra: Developing understandings of multiplication and division and strategies for basic multiplication facts and related division facts (p. 16).	*See* Grades 3–5 Multiplication and Division *for an essential understanding of*— • division defined in terms of its inverse relationship with multiplication; • the use of proper terminology and the division algorithm as the basis for the use of quotient and remainder in a division situation; • the use of the commutative and associative properties of multiplication and the distributive property of multiplication over addition to ensure flexibility in computation; • the use of the right (not left) distributive property of division over addition in the absence of associative and commutative properties of division to ensure flexibility in computation.

CCSSM Critical Area	*Principles and Standards* For information about instructional goals related to the mathematics content in this critical area	*Curriculum Focal Points* For information about how this content appears within an example of a focused curriculum proposed by NCTM	Essential Understanding Series For an articulation of mathematical understanding that is essential for teachers working in this critical area
(1) Developing understanding and fluency with multi-digit multiplication, and developing understanding of dividing to find quotients involving multi-digit dividends	*See* Grades 3–5 Algebra— Represent and analyze mathematical situations and structures using algebraic symbols (pp. 160–62), *regarding the expectation that students*— • identify such properties as commutativity, associativity, and distributivity and use them to compute with whole numbers; • represent the idea of a variable as an unknown quantity using a letter or a symbol; • express mathematical relationships using equations. *See* Grades 3–5 Algebra— Use mathematical models to represent and understand quantitative relationships (pp. 162–63), *regarding the expectation that students*— • model problem situations with objects and use representations such as graphs, tables, and equations to draw conclusions.		
(2) Developing an understanding of fraction equivalence, addition and subtraction of fractions with like denominators, and multiplication of fractions by whole numbers	*See* Grades 3–5 Number and Operations— Understand numbers, ways of representing numbers, relationships among numbers, and number systems (pp. 149–51), *regarding the expectation that students*— • use models, benchmarks, and equivalent forms to judge the size of fractions; • recognize and generate equivalent forms of commonly used fractions.... *See* Grades 3–5 Number and Operations— Compute fluently and make reasonable estimates (pp. 152–56), *regarding the expectation that students*— • develop and use strategies to estimate computations involving fractions ... in situations relevant to students' experience; • use visual models, benchmarks, and equivalent forms to add and subtract commonly used fractions....	*For an example of the placement of developing understanding of equivalent fractions in a focused curriculum, see* Grade 3 Focal Point for Number and Operations: Developing an understanding of fractions and fraction equivalence (p. 15). *For an example of the placement of developing understanding of addition and subtraction of fractions in a focused curriculum, see* Grade 5 Focal Point for Number and Operations: Developing an understanding of and fluency with addition and subtraction of fractions and decimals (p. 17).	*See* Grades 3–5 Rational Numbers *for an essential understanding of*— • equivalence of rational numbers, including generating an infinite number of equivalent fractions and comparing fractions (pp. 30–34); • operations on rational numbers as an extension of operations on whole numbers that introduces some new ideas and processes (pp. 42–55); • ways to help students make the shift from rational number comparisons based on whole numbers to comparisons based on equivalence (pp. 75–76).

CCSSM Critical Area	Principles and Standards For information about instructional goals related to the mathematics content in this critical area	Curriculum Focal Points For information about how this content appears within an example of a focused curriculum proposed by NCTM	Essential Understanding Series For an articulation of mathematical understanding that is essential for teachers working in this critical area
(2) Developing an understanding of fraction equivalence, addition and subtraction of fractions with like denominators, and multiplication of fractions by whole numbers	*See* Grades 6–8 Number and Operations— Compute fluently and make reasonable estimates (pp. 220–21), *regarding the expectation that students*— • select appropriate methods and tools for computing with fractions and decimals from among mental computation, estimation, calculators or computers, and paper and pencil, depending on the situation, and apply the selected methods; • develop and analyze algorithms for computing with fractions,… and develop fluency in their use; • develop and use strategies to estimate the results of rational number computations and judge the reasonableness of the results.	*For an example of the placement of developing understanding of multiplication of fractions in a focused curriculum, see* Grade 6 Focal Point for Number and Operations: Developing an understanding of and fluency with multiplication and division of fractions and decimals (p. 18).	
(3) Understanding that geometric figures can be analyzed and classified based on their properties, such as having parallel sides, perpendicular sides, particular angle measures, and symmetry	*See* Grades 3–5 Geometry— Analyze characteristics and properties of two- and three-dimensional geometric shapes and develop mathematical arguments about geometric relationships (pp. 165–66), *regarding the expectation that students*— • identify, compare, and analyze attributes of two- and three-dimensional shapes and develop vocabulary to describe the attributes; • classify two- and three-dimensional shapes according to their properties and develop definitions of classes of shapes such as triangles and pyramids. *See* Grades 3–5 Measurement— Apply appropriate techniques, tools, and formulas to determine measurements (pp. 173–75), *regarding the expectation that students*— • select and apply appropriate standard units and tools to measure length, area, volume, weight, time, temperature, and the size of angles.	*For an example of the placement of analyzing the properties of geometric figures in a focused curriculum, see* Grade 3 Focal Point for Geometry: Describing and analyzing properties of two-dimensional shapes (p. 15).	**Projected:** *See* Grades 3–5 Geometry (anticipated 2012) *for underlying ideas about*— • two-dimensional shapes.

Interpreting CCSSM for Grade 5

CCSSM Critical Area	Principles and Standards For information about instructional goals related to the mathematics content in this critical area	Curriculum Focal Points For information about how this content appears within an example of a focused curriculum proposed by NCTM	Essential Understanding Series For an articulation of mathematical understanding that is essential for teachers working in this critical area
(1) Developing fluency with addition and subtraction of fractions, and developing understanding of the multiplication of fractions and of division of fractions in limited cases (unit fractions divided by whole numbers and whole numbers divided by unit fractions)	See Grades 6–8 Number and Operations— Understand meanings of operations and how they relate to one another (pp. 218–20), regarding the expectation that students— • understand the meaning and effects of arithmetic operations with fractions, decimals, and integers; • use the associative and commutative properties of addition and multiplication and the distributive property of multiplication over addition to simplify computations with integers, fractions, and decimals. See Grades 6–8 Number and Operations— Compute fluently and make reasonable estimates (pp. 220–21), regarding the expectation that students— • select appropriate methods and tools for computing with fractions and decimals from among mental computation, estimation, calculators or computers, and paper and pencil, depending on the situation, and apply the selected methods; • develop and analyze algorithms for computing with fractions, decimals, and integers and develop fluency in their use; • develop and use strategies to estimate the results of rational number computations and judge the reasonableness of the results.	For an example of the placement of developing fluency with addition and subtraction of fractions in a focused curriculum, see Grade 5 Focal Point for Number and Operations: Developing an understanding of and fluency with addition and subtraction of fractions and decimals (p. 17). For an example of the placement of developing understanding of multiplication and division of fractions in a focused curriculum, see Grade 6 Focal Point for Number and Operations: Developing an understanding of and fluency with multiplication and division of fractions and decimals (p. 18).	See Grades 3–5 Rational Numbers for an essential understanding of— • operations on rational numbers as an extension of operations on whole numbers that introduces some new ideas and processes (pp. 42–55).
(2) Extending division to 2-digit divisors, integrating decimal fractions into the place value system and developing understanding of operations with decimals to hundredths, and developing fluency with whole number and decimal operations	See Grades 3–5 Number and Operations— Understand numbers, ways of representing numbers, relationships among numbers, and number systems (pp. 149–51), regarding the expectation that students— • understand the place-value structure of the base-ten number system and be able to represent and compare whole numbers and decimals. See Grades 3–5 Number and Operations— Compute fluently and make reasonable estimates (pp. 152–56), regarding the expectation that students— • develop fluency in adding, subtracting, multiplying, and dividing whole numbers; • develop and use strategies to estimate the results of whole number computations and to judge the reasonableness of such results;	For an example of developing fluency with division of whole numbers in a focused curriculum, see Grade 5 Focal Point for Number and Operations and Algebra: Developing an understanding of and fluency with division of whole numbers (p. 17). For an example of developing understanding of decimals in a focused curriculum, see Grade 4 Focal Point for Number and Operations: Developing an understanding of decimals, including the connections between fractions and decimals (p. 16).	See Grades 3–5 Multiplication and Division for an essential understanding of— • the use of a scalar definition of multiplication in representing and solving problems beyond whole number multiplication and division; • the connection of multiplication and division to percent. See Grades 3–5 Rational Numbers (2010) for an essential understanding of— • rational numbers as a natural extension of our base-ten number system (pp. 37–38);

CCSSM Critical Area	Principles and Standards For information about instructional goals related to the mathematics content in this critical area	Curriculum Focal Points For information about how this content appears within an example of a focused curriculum proposed by NCTM	Essential Understanding Series For an articulation of mathematical understanding that is essential for teachers working in this critical area
(2) Extending division to 2-digit divisors, integrating decimal fractions into the place value system and developing understanding of operations with decimals to hundredths, and developing fluency with whole number and decimal operations	• select appropriate methods and tools for computing with whole numbers from among mental computation, estimation, calculators, and paper and pencil according to the context and nature of the computation and use the selected method or tool. *See* Grades 3–5 Algebra— Represent and analyze mathematical situations and structures using algebraic symbols (pp. 160–62), *regarding the expectation that students*— • identify such properties as commutativity, associativity, and distributivity and use them to compute with whole numbers; • represent the idea of a variable as an unknown quantity using a letter or a symbol; • express mathematical relationships using equations. *See* Grades 3–5 Algebra— Use mathematical models to represent and understand quantitative relationships (pp. 160–62), *regarding the expectation that students*— • model problem situations with objects and use representations such as graphs, tables, and equations to draw conclusions. *See* Grades 6–8 Number and Operations— Understand meanings of operations and how they relate to one another (pp. 218–20), *regarding the expectation that students*— • understand the meaning and effects of arithmetic operations with fractions, decimals, and integers; • use the associative and commutative properties of addition and multiplication and the distributive property of multiplication over addition to simplify computations with integers, fractions, and decimals. *See* Grades 6–8 Number and Operations— Compute fluently and make reasonable estimates (pp. 220–21), *regarding the expectation that students*—	*For an example of developing fluency with addition and subtraction of decimals in a focused curriculum, see* Grade 5 Focal Point for Number and Operations and Algebra: Developing an understanding of and fluency with addition and subtraction of fractions and decimals (p. 17). *For an example of the placement of developing understanding of multiplication and division of decimals in a focused curriculum, see* Grade 6 Focal Point for Number and Operations: Developing an understanding of and fluency with multiplication and division of fractions and decimals (p. 18).	• translating fractions into decimals with a connection to equivalent fractions (pp. 38–41).

Interpreting CCSSM for Grade 5—*Continued*

CCSSM Critical Area	Principles and Standards For information about instructional goals related to the mathematics content in this critical area	Curriculum Focal Points For information about how this content appears within an example of a focused curriculum proposed by NCTM	Essential Understanding Series For an articulation of mathematical understanding that is essential for teachers working in this critical area
(2) Extending division to 2-digit divisors, integrating decimal fractions into the place value system and developing understanding of operations with decimals to hundredths, and developing fluency with whole number and decimal operations	• select appropriate methods and tools for computing with fractions and decimals from among mental computation, estimation, calculators or computers, and paper and pencil, depending on the situation, and apply the selected methods; • develop and analyze algorithms for computing with fractions, and develop fluency in their use; • develop and use strategies to estimate the results of rational number computations and judge the reasonableness of the results.		
(3) Developing understanding of volume	*See* Grades 3–5 Geometry— Analyze characteristics and properties of two- and three-dimensional geometric shapes and develop mathematical arguments about geometric relationships (pp. 165–66), *regarding the expectation that students—* • identify, compare, and analyze attributes of two- and three-dimensional shapes and develop vocabulary to describe the attributes; • classify two- and three-dimensional shapes according to their properties and develop definitions of classes of shapes such as triangles and pyramids. *See* Grades 3–5 Measurement— Apply appropriate techniques, tools, and formulas to determine measurements (pp. 173–75), *regarding the expectation that students—* • select and apply appropriate standard units and tools to measure length, area, volume, weight, time, temperature, and the size of angles.	*For an example of the placement of developing an understanding of volume in a focused curriculum, see* Grade 5 Focal Point for Geometry and Measurement and Algebra: Describing three-dimensional shapes and analyzing their properties, including volume and surface area (p. 17). *For an example of the placement of understanding angle measurement in a focused curriculum, see* Grade 4 Connections for Measurement: As part of understanding two-dimensional shapes, students measure and classify angles (p. 16).	**Projected:** *See* Grades 3–5 Geometry (anticipated 2012) *for underlying ideas about—* • the volume of three-dimensional shapes.

Interpreting CCSSM for Grade 6

CCSSM Critical Area	*Principles and Standards* For information about instructional goals related to the mathematics content in this critical area	*Curriculum Focal Points* For information about how this content appears within an example of a focused curriculum proposed by NCTM	*Essential Understanding Series* For an articulation of mathematical understanding that is essential for teachers working in this critical area
(1) Connecting ratio and rate to whole number multiplication and division and using concepts of ratio and rate to solve problems	*See* Grades 6–8 Number and Operations— Understand numbers, ways of representing numbers, relationships among numbers, and number systems (pp. 215–18), *regarding the expectation that students—* • understand and use ratios and proportions to represent quantitative relationships. *See* Grades 6–8 Number and Operations— Compute fluently and make reasonable estimates (pp. 220–21), *regarding the expectation that students—* • develop, analyze, and explain methods for solving problems involving proportions, such as scaling and finding equivalent ratios.	*For more about expectations regarding the connection of multiplication and division to rate and ratio, see* Grade 6 Focal Point for Number and Operations: Connecting ratio and rate to multiplication and division (p. 18).	*See* Grades 6–8 Ratios, Proportions, and Proportional Reasoning *for an essential understanding of—* • ratio as a multiplicative comparison of two quantities and as a joining of two quantities in a composed unit (pp. 18–22); • the importance of isolating the appropriate real-world attribute in a problem-solving situation (pp. 23–25). *See* Grades 3–5 Multiplication and Division *for an essential understanding of—* • a scalar definition of multiplication; • creating and interpreting multiplicative expressions developed in the context of a problem situation; • the use of a scalar definition of multiplication in representing and solving problems beyond whole number multiplication and division; • connecting multiplication as a fundamental operation to ratio tables; • connecting multiplication as a fundamental operation to similarity.
(2) Completing understanding of division of fractions and extending the notion of number to the system of rational numbers, which includes negative numbers	*See* Grades 6–8 Number and Operations— Understand numbers, ways of representing numbers, relationships among numbers, and number systems (pp. 215–18), *regarding the expectation that students—* • compare and order fractions, decimals, and percents efficiently and find their approximate locations on a number line; • develop meaning for integers and represent and compare quantities with them.	*For more about expectations regarding the meaning of multiplication and division and the relationships between these operations on whole numbers and between fractions and decimals, see* Grade 6 Focal Point for Number and Operations: Developing an understanding of and fluency with multiplication and division of fractions and decimals (p. 18).	*See* Grades 3–5 Rational Numbers *for an essential understanding of—* • extending from whole numbers to rational numbers, including rational numbers as quotients of whole numbers and examples of problems that can be solved with rational numbers beyond whole numbers (pp. 10–18);

CCSSM Critical Area	*Principles and Standards* For information about instructional goals related to the mathematics content in this critical area	*Curriculum Focal Points* For information about how this content appears within an example of a focused curriculum proposed by NCTM	*Essential Understanding Series* For an articulation of mathematical understanding that is essential for teachers working in this critical area
(2) Completing understanding of division of fractions and extending the notion of number to the system of rational numbers, which includes negative numbers	*See* Grades 6-8 Number and Operations— Compute fluently and make reasonable estimates (pp. 220–21), *regarding the expectation that students—* • select appropriate methods and tools for computing with fractions and decimals from among mental computation, estimation, calculators or computers, and paper and pencil, depending on the situation, and apply the selected methods; • develop and analyze algorithms for computing with fractions, decimals, and integers and develop fluency in their use.	*For expectations regarding the connection of whole number multiplication and division to multiplication and division with fractions and mixed numbers, see* Grade 6 Connection for Number and Operations (p. 18).	• ways in which experiences in pre-K– grade 2 and grades 3–5 with counting, unitizing, multiplication, fractions, division, decimals, and place value contribute to an extension of whole numbers to rational numbers (pp. 59–60); • extending from whole numbers and positive rational numbers to negative numbers, irrational numbers, real numbers, and beyond (pp. 66–68); • ways in which students make the shift from whole numbers to rational numbers (pp. 69–70).
(3) Writing, interpreting, and using expressions and equations	*See* Grades 6–8 Algebra— Understand patterns, relations, and functions (pp. 223–25), *regarding the expectation that students—* • represent, analyze, and generalize a variety of patterns with tables, graphs, words, and, when possible, symbolic rules. *See* Grades 6–8 Algebra— Represent and analyze mathematical situations and structures using algebraic symbols (pp. 225–27), *regarding the expectation that students—* • develop an initial conceptual understanding of different uses of variables; • use symbolic algebra to represent situations and to solve problems, especially those that involve linear relationships. *See* Grades 6–8 Algebra— Use mathematical models to represent and understand quantitative relationships (pp. 227–29), *regarding the expectation that students—* • model and solve contextualized problems using various representations, such as graphs, tables, and equations.	*For more about expectations regarding students' writing, reading, and solving of expressions and equations, see* Grade 6 Focal Point for Algebra: Writing, interpreting, and using mathematical expressions and equations (p. 18). *For expectations regarding identifying equivalent expressions, see* Grade 6 Connection for Algebra (p. 18).	*See* Grades 3–5 Algebraic Thinking *for an essential understanding of—* • using arithmetic as a context for algebraic reasoning; • decomposing algebraic expressions in meaningful ways; • the derivation of generalizations in arithmetic from fundamental properties of number systems; • the equals sign as a symbol of equivalence; • reasoning about equations as something more than a sequence of computations; • multiple interpretations of variables within expressions and equations; • functional thinking related to generalizing relationships between covarying quantities and expressing the relationships in symbols and other forms and reasoning with these representations.

Interpreting CCSSM for Grade 6—*Continued*

CCSSM Critical Area	*Principles and Standards* For information about instructional goals related to the mathematics content in this critical area	*Curriculum Focal Points* For information about how this content appears within an example of a focused curriculum proposed by NCTM	*Essential Understanding Series* For an articulation of mathematical understanding that is essential for teachers working in this critical area
(3) Writing, interpreting, and using expressions and equations	*See* Grades 6–8 Algebra— Analyze change in various contexts (pp. 229–31), *regarding the expectation that students—* • use graphs to analyze the nature of changes in quantities in linear relationships.		*See* Grades 6–8 Expressions, Equations, and Functions *for an essential understanding of—* • producing, interpreting, and using equivalent expressions.
(4) Developing understanding of statistical thinking	*See* Grades 6–8 Data Analysis and Probability— Formulate questions that can be addressed with data and collect, organize, and display relevant data to answer them (pp. 249–50), *regarding the expectation that students—* • formulate questions, design studies, and collect data about a characteristic shared by two populations or different characteristics within one population; • select, create, and use appropriate graphical representations of data, including histograms, box plots, and scatterplots. *See* Grades 6–8 Data Analysis and Probability— Select and use appropriate statistical methods to analyze data (pp. 250–51), *regarding the expectation that students—* • find, use, and interpret measures of center and spread, including mean and interquartile range; • discuss and understand the correspondence between data sets and their graphical representations, especially histograms, stem-and-leaf plots, box plots, and scatterplots.	*For more about expectations regarding measures of center and their use in representing a data set, see* Grade 8 Focal Point for Data Analysis *and* Number and Operations and Algebra: Analyzing and summarizing data sets (p. 20).	**Projected:** *See* Grades 6–8 Data (anticipated 2012) *for underlying ideas about—* • representing data; • interpreting data representations. **Projected:** *See* Grades 9–12 Statistics (anticipated 2012) *for an extended discussion of—* • using measures of center and spread to describe and compare samples and populations.

Interpreting CCSSM for Grade 7

CCSSM Critical Area	*Principles and Standards* For information about instructional goals related to the mathematics content in this critical area	*Curriculum Focal Points* For information about how this content appears within an example of a focused curriculum proposed by NCTM	Essential Understanding Series For an articulation of mathematical understanding that is essential for teachers working in this critical area
(1) Developing understanding of and applying proportional relationships	*See* Grades 6–8 Number and Operations— Understand numbers, ways of representing numbers, relationships among numbers, and number systems (pp. 215–18), *regarding the expectation that students—* • work flexibly with fractions, decimals, and percents to solve problems; • understand and use ratios and proportions to represent quantitative relationships. *See* Grades 6–8 Number and Operations— Compute fluently and make reasonable estimates (pp. 220–21), *regarding the expectation that students—* • develop, analyze, and explain methods for solving problems involving proportions, such as scaling and finding equivalent ratios.	*For nearly identical expectations regarding applying understanding of proportionality to solve problems of various types, relating proportionality to similarity and linearity, and distinguishing between proportional relationships and other relationships,* see *Grade 7 Focal Point for Number and Operations and Algebra and Geometry: Developing an understanding of and applying proportionality, including similarity (p. 19).*	*See* Grades 6–8 Ratios, Proportions, and Proportional Reasoning *for an essential understanding of—* • the differences and similarities between fractions and ratios, including part-whole and part-part relationships (pp. 26–30); • how ratios may be interpreted as quotients (pp. 31–32); • what proportions are and what they mean in the context of a real-world problem (pp. 33–35); • creating and interpreting equivalent ratios (pp. 36–41); • the meaning of *rate* in terms of equivalent ratios (pp. 42–43); • how different forms of reasoning can be generalized into algorithms for solving proportion problems (pp. 44–45).
(2) Developing understanding of operations with rational numbers and working with expressions and linear equations	*See* Grades 6–8 Number and Operations— Understand numbers, ways of representing numbers, relationships among numbers, and number systems (pp. 215–18), *regarding the expectation that students—* • work flexibly with fractions, decimals, and percents to solve problems; • develop meaning for integers and represent and compare quantities with them. *See* Grades 6-8 Number and Operations— Understand meanings of operations and how they relate to one another (pp. 218–20), *regarding the expectation that students—* • understand the meaning and effects of arithmetic operations with fractions, decimals, and integers;	*For nearly identical expectations about extending understanding of operations and their properties to all rational numbers, applying these ideas in everyday contexts, and using the arithmetic of rational numbers in generating and manipulating expressions and equations,* see *Grade 7 Focal Point for Number and Operations and Algebra: Developing an understanding of operations on all rational numbers and solving linear equations (p. 19).*	*See* Grades 3–5 Rational Numbers *for an essential understanding of—* • how computation with rational numbers extends computation with whole numbers but introduces some new ideas and processes (pp. 42–55). *See* Grades 6–8 Expressions, Equations, and Functions (2010) *for an essential understanding of—* • multiple interpretations of the equals sign; • different meanings of variables depending on context and purpose.

CCSSM Critical Area	*Principles and Standards* For information about instructional goals related to the mathematics content in this critical area	*Curriculum Focal Points* For information about how this content appears within an example of a focused curriculum proposed by NCTM	Essential Understanding Series For an articulation of mathematical understanding that is essential for teachers working in this critical area
(2) Developing understanding of operations with rational numbers and working with expressions and linear equations	• use the associative and commutative properties of addition and multiplication and the distributive property of multiplication over addition to simplify computations with integers, fractions, and decimals; • understand and use the inverse relationships of addition and subtraction, multiplication and division, and squaring and finding square roots to simplify computations and solve problems. *See* Grades 6–8 Number and Operations— Compute fluently and make reasonable estimates (pp. 220–21), *regarding the expectation that students—* • develop and analyze algorithms for computing with fractions, decimals, and integers and develop fluency in their use.	*For expectations regarding the connection of whole number multiplication and division to fractions and mixed numbers, see* Grade 7 Connection for Number and Operations (p. 19).	
(3) Solving problems involving scale drawings and informal geometric constructions, and working with two- and three-dimensional shapes to solve problems involving area, surface area, and volume	*See* Grades 6–8 Geometry— Analyze characteristics and properties of two- and three-dimensional geometric shapes and develop mathematical arguments about geometric relationships (pp. 233–35), *regarding the expectation that students—* • precisely describe, classify, and understand relationships among types of two- and three-dimensional objects using their defining properties; • understand relationships among the angles, side lengths, perimeters, areas, and volumes of similar objects.	*For more about expectations regarding surface area and volume of particular three-dimensional figures and the development and interpretation of relevant formulas, including the use of algebraic equations and expressions, see* Grade 7 Focal Point for Measurement and Geometry and Algebra: Developing an understanding of and using formulas to determine surface areas and volumes of three-dimensional shapes (p. 19).	**Projected:** See Grades 6–8 Geometry (forthcoming) *for a discussion of—* • two- and three-dimensional shapes; • scale; • relationships among area, surface area, and volume.

CCSSM Critical Area	Principles and Standards For information about instructional goals related to the mathematics content in this critical area	Curriculum Focal Points For information about how this content appears within an example of a focused curriculum proposed by NCTM	Essential Understanding Series For an articulation of mathematical understanding that is essential for teachers working in this critical area
(3) Solving problems involving scale drawings and informal geometric constructions, and working with two- and three-dimensional shapes to solve problems involving area, surface area, and volume	*See* Grades 6–8 Geometry— Use visualization, spatial reasoning, and geometric modeling to solve problems (pp. 237–39), *regarding the expectation that students—* • draw geometric objects with specified properties, such as side lengths or angle measures; • use two-dimensional representations of three-dimensional objects to visualize and solve problems such as those involving surface area and volume; • recognize and apply geometric ideas and relationships in areas outside the mathematics classroom, such as art, science, and everyday life.	*For extensions of understanding of two-dimensional shapes to three-dimensional shapes, including linking area to surface areas, see* Grade 7 Connection for Measurement and Geometry (p. 19).	**Projected:** *See* Grades 9–12 Geometry (anticipated 2012) *for an extended discussion of—* • geometric constructions.
(4) Drawing inferences about populations based on samples	*See* Grades 6–8 Data Analysis and Probability— Formulate questions that can be addressed with data and collect, organize, and display relevant data to answer them (pp. 249–50), *regarding the expectation that students—* • formulate questions, design studies, and collect data about a characteristic shared by two populations or different characteristics within one population. *See* Grades 6–8 Data Analysis and Probability— Develop and evaluate inferences and predictions that are based on data (pp. 251–53), *regarding the expectation that students—* • use observations about differences between two or more samples to make conjectures about the populations from which the samples were taken.	*For more about expectations regarding measures of center and their use in representing a data set, see* Grade 8 Focal Point for Data Analysis and Number and Operations and Algebra: Analyzing and summarizing data sets (p. 20). *For expectations regarding estimates relating to a population on the basis of a sample, see* Grade 7 Connection for Data Analysis (p. 19). *For expectations regarding theoretical probability and proportions, see* Grade 7 Connection for Probability (p. 19).	**Projected:** *See* Grades 6–8 Data (anticipated 2012) *for underlying ideas about—* • inference. **Projected:** *See* Grades 9–12 Statistics (anticipated 2012) *for an extended discussion of—* • inference based on samples.

Interpreting CCSSM for Grade 8

CCSSM Critical Area	Principles and Standards For information about instructional goals related to the mathematics content in this critical area	Curriculum Focal Points For information about how this content appears within an example of a focused curriculum proposed by NCTM	Essential Understanding Series For an articulation of mathematical understanding that is essential for teachers working in this critical area
(1) Formulating and reasoning about expressions and equations, including modeling an association in bivariate data with a linear equation, and solving linear equations and systems of linear equations	*See* Grades 6–8 Algebra— Represent and analyze mathematical situations and structures using algebraic symbols (pp. 225–27), *regarding the expectation that students—* • explore relationships between symbolic expressions and graphs of lines, paying particular attention to the meaning of intercept and slope.	*For more about the relationship of proportionality to linear equations, representations of linear relationships, and systems of linear equations and the application of these ideas in problem-solving settings, see* Grade 8 Focal Point for Algebra: Analyzing and representing linear functions and solving linear equations and systems of linear equations (p. 20).	*See* Grades 6–8 Expressions, Equations, and Functions (2011) *for an essential understanding of—* • using variables, expressions, and functions to represent relationships between quantities; • algorithms and methods for solving linear equations.
(2) Grasping the concept of a function and using functions to describe quantitative relationships	*See* Grades 6–8 Algebra— Understand patterns, relations, and functions (pp. 223–25), *regarding the expectation that students—* • relate and compare different forms of representation for a relationship; • identify functions as linear or nonlinear and contrast their properties from tables, graphs, or equations.	*For more about translating among representations of functions, see* Grade 8 Focal Point for Algebra: Analyzing and representing linear functions and solving linear equations and systems of linear equations (p. 20). *For expectations regarding the use of functions to describe quantitative relationships, see* Grade 8 Connection for Algebra (p. 20).	*See* Grades 6–8 Expressions, Equations, and Functions (2011) *for an essential understanding of—* • using rate of change and other characteristics of function families to model relationships among quantities. *See* Grades 9–12 Functions *for an essential understanding of—* • the function concept and definitions of *function* (pp. 12–22); • function families and their role in modeling real-world relationships (pp. 34–69).

CCSSM Critical Area	Principles and Standards For information about instructional goals related to the mathematics content in this critical area	Curriculum Focal Points For information about how this content appears within an example of a focused curriculum proposed by NCTM	Essential Understanding Series For an articulation of mathematical understanding that is essential for teachers working in this critical area
(3) Analyzing two- and three-dimensional space and figures using distance, angle, similarity, and congruence, and understanding and applying the Pythagorean theorem	*See* Grades 6–8 Geometry— Analyze characteristics and properties of two- and three-dimensional geometric shapes and develop mathematical arguments about geometric relationships (pp. 233–35), *regarding the expectation that students—* • precisely describe, classify, and understand relationships among types of two- and three-dimensional objects using their defining properties; • understand relationships among the angles, side lengths, perimeters, areas, and volumes of similar objects. *See* Grades 6–8 Geometry— Apply transformations and use symmetry to analyze mathematical situations (pp. 235–37), *regarding the expectation that students—* • describe sizes, positions, and orientations of shapes under informal transformations such as flips, turns, slides, and scaling.	*For a similar expectation involving distance, angle, similar triangles and the Pythagorean theorem, see* Grade 8 Focal Point for Geometry and Measurement: Analyzing two- and three-dimensional space and figures by using distance and angle (p. 20).	**Projected:** *See* Grades 6–8 Geometry (forthcoming) *for a discussion of—* • two- and three-dimensional shapes, angle, distance, similarity, and the Pythagorean theorem.

Sample Interpretation Chart for High School

Interpreting CCSSM for High School in the Conceptual Category of Functions

CCSSM Cluster of Standards, Identified by Domain	*Principles and Standards* For information about instructional goals related to the mathematics content in this cluster	*Focus in High School Mathematics* For information about promoting reasoning and sense making within this cluster	Essential Understanding Series For an articulation of mathematical understanding that is essential for teachers working in this cluster
Interpreting Functions			
• Understand the concept of a function and use function notation	*See* Grades 9–12 Algebra— Understand patterns, relations, and functions (pp. 297–300), *regarding the expectation that students—* • generalize patterns using explicitly defined and recursively defined functions.	Reasoning with Functions • Modeling by using families of functions	*See* Grades 9–12 Functions—Big Idea 1: The concept of function is intentionally broad and flexible, allowing it to apply to a wide range of situations. The notion of function encompasses many types of mathematical entities in addition to "classical" functions that describe quantities that vary continuously. For example, matrices and arithmetic and geometric sequences can be viewed as functions.
• Interpret functions that arise in applications in terms of the context	*See* Grades 9–12 Algebra— Understand patterns, relations, and functions (pp. 297–300), *regarding the expectation that students—* • analyze functions of one variable by investigating rates of change, intercepts, zeros, asymptotes, and local and global behavior. *See* Grades 9–12 Algebra— Use mathematical models to represent and understand quantitative relationships (p. 303–5), *regarding the expectation that students—* • identify essential quantitative relationships in a situation and determine the class or classes of functions that might model the relationships. *See* Grades 9–12 Algebra— Analyze change in various contexts (p. 305–6), *regarding the expectation that students—* • approximate and interpret rates of change from graphical and numerical data.	Reasoning with Functions • Modeling by using families of functions	*See* Grades 9–12 Functions—Big Idea 2: Functions provide a means to describe how related quantities vary together. We can classify, predict, and characterize various kinds of relationships by attending to the rate at which one quantity varies with respect to the other.

Interpreting CCSSM for High School in the Conceptual Category of Functions—*Continued*

CCSSM Cluster of Standards, Identified by Domain	*Principles and Standards* For information about instructional goals related to the mathematics content in this cluster	*Focus in High School Mathematics* For information about promoting reasoning and sense making within this cluster	Essential Understanding Series For an articulation of mathematical understanding that is essential for teachers working in this cluster
Interpreting Functions			
• Analyze functions using different representations	*See* Grades 9–12 Algebra— Understand patterns, relations, and functions (pp. 297–300), *regarding the expectation that students*— • understand relations and functions and select, convert flexibly among, and use various representations for them. *See* Grades 9–12 Algebra— Represent and analyze mathematical situations and structures using algebraic symbols (pp. 300–303), *regarding the expectation that students*— • understand the meaning of equivalent forms of expressions, equations, inequalities, and relations.	Reasoning with Functions • Analyzing the effects of parameters	*See* Grades 9–12 Functions—Big Idea 5: Functions can be represented in multiple ways, including algebraic (symbolic), graphical, verbal, and tabular representations. Links among these different representations are important to studying relationships and change.
Building Functions			
• Build a function that models a relationship between two quantities	*See* Grades 9–12 Algebra— Understand patterns, relations, and functions (pp. 297–300), *regarding the expectation that students*— • generalize patterns using explicitly defined and recursively defined functions; • understand and perform transformations such as arithmetically combining, composing, and inverting commonly used functions, using technology to perform such operations on more complicated symbolic expressions.	Reasoning with Functions • Analyzing the effects of parameters	*See* Grades 9–12 Functions—Big Idea 4: Functions can be combined by adding, subtracting, multiplying, dividing, and composing them. Functions sometimes have inverses. Functions can often be analyzed by viewing them as made from other functions.

Interpreting CCSSM for High School in the Conceptual Category of Functions—*Continued*

CCSSM Cluster of Standards, Identified by Domain	*Principles and Standards* For information about instructional goals related to the mathematics content in this cluster	*Focus in High School Mathematics* For information about promoting reasoning and sense making within this cluster	Essential Understanding Series For an articulation of mathematical understanding that is essential for teachers working in this cluster
Building Functions			
• Build new functions from existing functions	*See* Grades 9–12 Algebra— Understand patterns, relations, and functions (pp. 297–300), *regarding the expectation that students—* • understand and perform transformations such as arithmetically combining, composing, and inverting commonly used functions, using technology to perform such operations on more complicated symbolic expressions.	Reasoning with Functions • Analyzing the effects of parameters	*See* Grades 9–12 Functions—Big Idea 4: Functions can be combined by adding, subtracting, multiplying, dividing, and composing them. Functions sometimes have inverses. Functions can often be analyzed by viewing them as made from other functions.
Linear, Quadratic, and Exponential Models			
• Construct and compare linear, quadratic, and exponential models and solve problems	*See* Grades 9–12 Algebra— Understand patterns, relations, and functions (pp. 297–300), *regarding the expectation that students—* • understand and compare the properties of classes of functions, including exponential, polynomial, rational, logarithmic, and periodic functions. *See* Grades 9–12 Algebra— Use mathematical models to represent and understand quantitative relationships (pp. 303–5), *regarding the expectation that students—* • use symbolic expressions, including iterative and recursive forms, to represent relationships arising from various contexts. *See* Grades 9–12 Algebra— Analyze change in various contexts (pp. 305–6), *regarding the expectation that students—* • approximate and interpret rates of change from graphical and numerical data.	Reasoning with Functions • Modeling by using families of functions	*See* Grades 9–12 Functions—Big Idea 3: Functions can be classified into different families of functions, each with its own unique characteristics. Different families can be used to model different real-world phenomena.

Appendix A

89

CCSSM Cluster of Standards, Identified by Domain	*Principles and Standards* For information about instructional goals related to the mathematics content in this cluster	*Focus in High School Mathematics* For information about promoting reasoning and sense making within this cluster	Essential Understanding Series For an articulation of mathematical understanding that is essential for teachers working in this cluster
Linear, Quadratic, and Exponential Models			
• Interpret expressions for functions in terms of the situation they model	*See* Grades 9–12 Algebra— Use mathematical models to represent and understand quantitative relationships (pp. 303–5), *regarding the expectation that students—* • draw reasonable conclusions about a situation being modeled. *See* Grades 9–12 Algebra— Understand patterns, relations, and functions (pp. 297–300), *regarding the expectation that students—* • understand and compare the properties of classes of functions, including exponential, polynomial, rational, logarithmic, and periodic functions.	Reasoning with Functions • Modeling by using families of functions	*See* Grades 9–12 Functions—Big Idea 2: Functions provide a means to describe how related quantities vary together. We can classify, predict, and characterize various kinds of relationships by attending to the rate at which one quantity varies with respect to the other.
Trigonometric Functions			
• Extend the domain of trigonometric functions using the unit circle	*See* Grades 9–12 Algebra— Understand patterns, relations, and functions pp. 297–300), *regarding the expectation that students—* • understand and compare the properties of classes of functions, including exponential, polynomial, rational, logarithmic, and periodic functions.	Reasoning with Functions • Modeling by using families of functions	*See* Grades 9–12 Functions (pp. 59–69) for a discussion of— • trigonometric ratios based on the unit circle.
• Model periodic phenomena with trigonometric functions	*See* Grades 9–12 Algebra— Understand patterns, relations, and functions (pp. 297–300), *regarding the expectation that students—*	Reasoning with Functions • Modeling by using families of functions	*See* Grades 9–12 Functions—Big Idea 3: Functions can be classified into different families of functions, each with its own unique characteristics. Different families can be used to model different real-world phenomena.

Interpreting CCSSM for High School in the Conceptual Category of Functions—*Continued*

CCSSM Cluster of Standards, Identified by Domain	*Principles and Standards* For information about instructional goals related to the mathematics content in this cluster	*Focus in High School Mathematics* For information about promoting reasoning and sense making within this cluster	**Essential Understanding Series** For an articulation of mathematical understanding that is essential for teachers working in this cluster
Trigonometric Functions			
	• understand and compare the properties of classes of functions, including exponential, polynomial, rational, logarithmic, and periodic functions; • understand and perform transformations such as arithmetically combining, composing, and inverting commonly used functions, using technology to perform such operations on more complicated symbolic expressions. *See* Grades 9–12 Algebra— Use mathematical models to represent and understand quantitative relationships (pp. 303–5), *regarding the expectation that students*— • identify essential quantitative relationships in a situation and determine the class or classes of functions that might model the relationships; • use symbolic expressions, including iterative and recursive forms, to represent relationships arising from various contexts; • draw reasonable conclusions about a situation being modeled.		
• Prove and apply trigonometric identities	*See* Grades 9–12 Algebra— Represent and analyze mathematical situations and structures using algebraic symbols (pp. 300–303), *regarding the expectation that students*— • use symbolic algebra to represent and explain mathematical relationships.	Reasoning with Geometry • Construction and evaluation of geometric arguments	**Projected:** *See* Grades 9–12 Proof and Proving (anticipated 2012) *for a discussion of*— • proofs and proving in trigonometry.

Appendix B

Mathematical Practices and Processes Chart

CCSSM— Standard for Mathematical Practice, including commentary	Principles and Standards— Process Standard, including areas of emphasis	Focus in High School Mathematics— Reasoning Habit
1. Make sense of problems and persevere in solving them.		
Mathematically proficient students start by explaining to themselves the meaning of a problem and looking for entry points to its solution.	Problem Solving— • apply and adapt a variety of appropriate strategies to solve problems.	Analyzing a problem— • identifying relevant mathematical concepts, procedures, or representations that reveal important information about the problem and contribute to its solution.
Proficient students analyze givens, constraints, relationships, and goals.	Problem Solving— • apply and adapt a variety of appropriate strategies to solve problems.	Analyzing a problem— • defining relevant variables and conditions carefully, including units if appropriate.
Proficient students make conjectures about the form and meaning of the solution and plan a solution pathway rather than simply jumping into a solution attempt.	Problem Solving— • apply and adapt a variety of appropriate strategies to solve problems. Reasoning and Proof— • make and investigate mathematical conjectures.	Analyzing a problem— • making preliminary deductions and conjectures, including predicting what a solution to a problem might involve or putting constraints on solutions.
Proficient students consider analogous problems, and try special cases and simpler forms of the original problem in order to gain insight into its solution.	Problem Solving— • apply and adapt a variety of appropriate strategies to solve problems.	Analyzing a problem— • considering special cases or simpler analogs Seeking and using connections across … different contexts.
Proficient students monitor and evaluate their progress and change course if necessary.	Problem Solving— • monitor and reflect on the process of mathematical problem solving.	Implementing a strategy— • monitoring progress toward a solution, including reviewing a chosen strategy and other possible strategies generated by oneself or others.
Older students might, depending on the context of the problem, transform algebraic expressions or change the viewing window on their graphing calculator to get the information they need.	Representation— • create and use representations to organize, record, and communicate mathematical ideas.	Analyzing a problem— • looking for hidden structure.
Mathematically proficient students can explain correspondences between equations, verbal descriptions, tables, and graphs or draw diagrams of important features and relationships, graph data, and search for regularity or trends.	Representation— • select, apply, and translate among mathematical representations to solve problems.	Seeking and using connections across … different representations.

CCSSM— Standard for Mathematical Practice, including commentary	Principles and Standards— Process Standard, including areas of emphasis	Focus in High School Mathematics— Reasoning Habit
Younger students might rely on using concrete objects or pictures to help conceptualize and solve a problem.	Representation— • use representations to model and interpret physical, social, and mathematical phenomena.	Seeking and using connections across … different representations.
Mathematically proficient students check their answers to problems using a different method, and they continually ask themselves, "Does this make sense?"	Problem Solving— • monitor and reflect on the process of mathematical problem solving.	Reflecting on a solution— • reconciling different approaches to solving the problem, including those proposed by others.
Proficient students can understand the approaches of others to solving complex problems and identify correspondences between different approaches.	Communication— • analyze and evaluate the mathematical thinking and strategies of others.	Reflecting on a solution— • reconciling different approaches to solving the problem, including those proposed by others.

2. Reason abstractly and quantitatively.

Mathematically proficient students make sense of quantities and their relationships in problem situations.	Problem Solving— • apply and adapt a variety of appropriate strategies to solve problems.	Analyzing a problem— • defining relevant variables and conditions carefully, including units if appropriate. Reflecting on a solution— • considering the reasonableness of a solution, including whether any numbers are reported at an unreasonable level of accuracy.
Proficient students bring two complementary abilities to bear on problems involving quantitative relationships: the ability to *decontextualize* and the ability to *contextualize*.	Problem Solving— • apply and adapt a variety of appropriate strategies to solve problems.	Analyzing a problem.
Quantitative reasoning entails habits of creating a coherent representation of the problem at hand; considering the units involved; attending to the meaning of quantities, not just how to compute them; and knowing and flexibly using different properties of operations and objects.	Problem Solving— • apply and adapt a variety of appropriate strategies to solve problems; • monitor and reflect on the process of mathematical problem solving.	Analyzing a problem— • applying previously learned concepts to new problem situations, adapting and extending as necessary.

3. Construct viable arguments and critique the reasoning of others.

Mathematically proficient students understand and use stated assumptions, definitions, and previously established results in constructing arguments.	Reasoning and Proof— • make and investigate mathematical conjectures; • develop and evaluate mathematical arguments and proofs.	Analyzing a problem— • applying previously learned concepts to new problem situations, adapting and extending as necessary; • defining relevant variables and conditions carefully, including units if appropriate.

CCSSM— Standard for Mathematical Practice, including commentary	Principles and Standards— Process Standard, including areas of emphasis	Focus in High School Mathematics— Reasoning Habit
Proficient students make conjectures and build a logical progression of statements to explore the truth of their conjectures.	Reasoning and Proof— • make and investigate mathematical conjectures; • develop and evaluate mathematical arguments and proofs.	Implementing a strategy— • making logical deductions based on current progress, verifying conjectures, and extending initial findings.
Proficient students are able to analyze situations by breaking them into cases, and can recognize and use counterexamples.	Reasoning and Proof— • select and use various types of reasoning and methods of proof.	Implementing a strategy— • organizing the solution.
Proficient students justify their conclusions, communicate them to others, and respond to the arguments of others.	Communication— • organize and consolidate ... mathematical thinking through communication; • communicate ... mathematical thinking coherently and clearly to peers, teachers, and others.	Reflecting on a solution— • justifying or validating a solution; • reconciling different approaches to solving the problem, including those proposed by others; • refining arguments so that they can be effectively communicated.
Proficient students reason inductively about data, making plausible arguments that take into account the context from which the data arose.	Reasoning and Proof • select and use various types of reasoning and methods of proof.	Analyzing a problem— • deciding whether a statistical approach is appropriate. Reflecting on a solution— • interpreting a solution and how it answers the problem, including making decisions under uncertain conditions; • recognizing the scope of inference for a statistical solution.
Mathematically proficient students are also able to compare the effectiveness of two plausible arguments, distinguish correct logic or reasoning from that which is flawed, and—if there is a flaw in an argument—explain what it is.	Communication— • analyze and evaluate the mathematical thinking and strategies of others.	Reflecting on a solution— • reconciling different approaches to solving the problem, including those proposed by others.
Elementary students can construct arguments using concrete referents such as objects, drawings, diagrams, and actions. Such arguments can make sense and be correct, even though they are not generalized or made formal until later grades.	Representation— • create and use representations to organize, record, and communicate mathematical ideas.	

CCSSM— Standard for Mathematical Practice, including commentary	Principles and Standards— Process Standard, including areas of emphasis	Focus in High School Mathematics— Reasoning Habit
Later, students learn to determine domains to which an argument applies.	Problem Solving— • monitor and reflect on the process of mathematical problem solving.	Reflecting on a solution— • revisiting initial assumptions about the nature of the solution, including being mindful of special cases and extraneous solutions; • generalizing a solution to a broader class of problems and looking for connections with other problems.
Students at all grades can listen or read the arguments of others, decide whether they make sense, and ask useful questions to clarify or improve the arguments.	Reasoning and Proof— • develop and evaluate mathematical arguments and proofs.	Reflecting on a solution— • reconciling different approaches to solving the problem, including those proposed by others; • refining arguments so that they can be effectively communicated.

4. Model with mathematics.

Mathematically proficient students can apply the mathematics they know to solve problems arising in everyday life, society, and the workplace.	Problem Solving— • solve problems that arise in mathematics and in other contexts. Connections— • recognize and apply mathematics in contexts outside of mathematics. Representation— • recognize and apply mathematics in contexts outside of mathematics.	Seeking and using connections across different mathematical domains.
Mathematically proficient students who can apply what they know are comfortable making assumptions and approximations to simplify a complicated situation, realizing that these may need revision later.	Connections— • recognize and use connections among mathematical ideas.	Analyzing a problem— • making preliminary deductions and conjectures, including predicting what a solution to a problem might involve or putting constraints on solutions.
Proficient students are able to identify important quantities in a practical situation and map their relationships using such tools as diagrams, two-way tables, graphs, flowcharts and formulas.	Representation— • select, apply, and translate among mathematical representations to solve problems; • use representations to model and interpret physical, social, and mathematical phenomena.	Analyzing a problem— • defining relevant variables and conditions carefully, including units if appropriate.

CCSSM— Standard for Mathematical Practice, including commentary	Principles and Standards— Process Standard, including areas of emphasis	Focus in High School Mathematics— Reasoning Habit
Mathematically proficient students can analyze those relationships mathematically to draw conclusions.	Reasoning and Proof— • develop and evaluate mathematical arguments and proofs.	Analyzing a problem— • seeking patterns and relationships.
Proficient students routinely interpret their mathematical results in the context of the situation and reflect on whether the results make sense, possibly improving the model if it has not served its purpose.	Problem Solving— • monitor and reflect on the process of mathematical problem solving. Representation— • use representations to model and interpret physical, social, and mathematical phenomena.	Reflecting on a solution— • interpreting a solution and how it answers the problem, including making decisions under uncertain conditions.
5. Use appropriate tools strategically.		
Mathematically proficient students consider the available tools when solving a mathematical problem.	Representation— • Create and use representations to organize, record, and communicate mathematical ideas.	Analyzing a problem— • identifying relevant concepts, procedures, or representations.
Proficient students are sufficiently familiar with tools appropriate for their grade or course to make sound decisions about when each of these tools might be helpful, recognizing both the insight to be gained and their limitations.	Representation— • create and use representations to organize, record, and communicate mathematical ideas.	Analyzing a problem— • identifying relevant concepts, procedures, or representations.
Proficient students detect possible errors by strategically using estimation and other mathematical knowledge.	Problem Solving— • monitor and reflect on the process of mathematical problem solving.	Reflecting on a solution— • considering the reasonableness of a solution, including whether any numbers are reported at an unreasonable level of accuracy.
When making mathematical models, proficient students know that technology can enable them to visualize the results of varying assumptions, explore consequences, and compare predictions with data.	Representation— • use representations to model and interpret physical, social, and mathematical phenomena.	Analyzing a problem— • identifying relevant concepts, procedures, or representations.
Mathematically proficient students at various grade levels are able to identify relevant external mathematical resources, such as digital content located on a website, and use them to pose or solve problems.	Problem Solving— • monitor and reflect on the process of mathematical problem solving.	Analyzing a problem— • identifying relevant concepts, procedures, or representations.

CCSSM— Standard for Mathematical Practice, including commentary	Principles and Standards— Process Standard, including areas of emphasis	Focus in High School Mathematics— Reasoning Habit
Proficient students are able to use technological tools to explore and deepen their understanding of concepts.	Representation— • select, apply, and translate among mathematical representations to solve problems.	Analyzing a problem— • identifying relevant concepts, procedures, or representations.

6. Attend to precision.

Mathematically proficient students try to communicate precisely to others.	Communication— • use the language of mathematics to express mathematical ideas precisely.	Reflecting on a solution— • refining arguments so that they can be effectively communicated.
Proficient students try to use clear definitions in discussion with others and in their own reasoning.	Communication— • use the language of mathematics to express mathematical ideas precisely.	Reflecting on a solution— • refining arguments so that they can be effectively communicated.
Proficient students state the meaning of the symbols they choose, including using the equal sign consistently and appropriately.	Communication— • use the language of mathematics to express mathematical ideas precisely.	Analyzing a problem— • defining relevant variables and conditions carefully, including units if appropriate.
Proficient students are careful about specifying units of measure, and labeling axes to clarify the correspondence with quantities in a problem.	Communication— • use the language of mathematics to express mathematical ideas precisely.	Analyzing a problem— • defining relevant variables and conditions carefully, including units if appropriate.
Proficient students calculate accurately and efficiently, express numerical answers with a degree of precision appropriate for the problem context.	Problem Solving— • monitor and reflect on the process of mathematical problem solving.	Reflecting on a solution— • considering the reasonableness of a solution, including whether any numbers are reported at an unreasonable level of accuracy.
In the elementary grades, students give carefully formulated explanations to each other.	Communication— • use the language of mathematics to express mathematical ideas precisely.	Reflecting on a solution— • refining arguments so that they can be effectively communicated.
By the time students reach high school they have learned to examine claims and make explicit use of definitions.	Communication— • use the language of mathematics to express mathematical ideas precisely.	Reflecting on a solution— • refining arguments so that they can be effectively communicated.

7. Look for and make use of structure.

Mathematically proficient students look closely to discern a pattern or structure.	Reasoning and Proof— • make and investigate mathematical conjectures.	Analyzing a problem— • seeking patterns and relationships; • looking for hidden structure.

CCSSM—Standard for Mathematical Practice, including commentary	Principles and Standards—Process Standard, including areas of emphasis	Focus in High School Mathematics—Reasoning Habit
Proficient students also can step back for an overview and shift perspective.	Problem Solving— • monitor and reflect on the process of mathematical problem solving.	Implementing a strategy— • monitoring progress toward a solution, including reviewing a chosen strategy and other possible strategies generated by oneself or others.
Proficient students can see complicated things, such as some algebraic expressions, as single objects or as being composed of several objects.	Connections— • recognize and use connections among mathematical ideas.	Analyzing a problem— • looking for hidden structure.
8. Look for and express regularity in repeated reasoning.		
Mathematically proficient students notice if calculations are repeated, and look both for general methods and for shortcuts.	Connections— • recognize and use connections among mathematical ideas.	Analyzing a problem • seeking patterns and relationships.
As they work to solve a problem, mathematically proficient students maintain oversight of the process, while attending to the details.	Problem Solving— • monitor and reflect on the process of mathematical problem solving.	Implementing a strategy— • making purposeful use of procedures; • organizing the solution, including calculations, algebraic manipulations, and data displays.
Proficient students continually evaluate the reasonableness of their intermediate results.	Problem Solving— • monitor and reflect on the process of mathematical problem solving.	Implementing a strategy— • monitoring progress toward a solution, including reviewing a chosen strategy and other possible strategies generated by oneself or others.

Interpreting the Common Core State Standards to Improve Mathematics Education

References

Achieve. *American Diploma Project.* Washington, D.C.: Achieve, 2003.

———. *Rising to the Challenge: Are High School Graduates Prepared for College and Work?* Washington, D.C.: Achieve, 2005.

———. *Closing the Expectations Gap 2011: Sixth Annual 50-State Progress Report on the Alignment of High School Policies with the Demands of College and Careers.* Washington, D.C.: Achieve, 2011.

ACT. *Ready for College or Ready for Work: Same or Different?* Iowa City, Iowa: American College Testing Service, 2006.

Adelman, Clifford. *The Toolbox Revisited: Paths to Degree Completion from High School through College.* Washington, D.C: U.S. Department of Education, 2006.

Baker, Scott, Russell Gersten, and Dae-Sik Lee. "A Synthesis of Empirical Research on Teaching Mathematics to Low-Achieving Students." *The Elementary School Journal* 103 (September 2002): 51–73.

Baldi, Stéphane, Ying Jin, Melanie Skemer, Patricia J. Green, and Deborah Herget. *Highlights from PISA 2006: Performance of U.S. 15-Year-Old Students in Science and Mathematics Literacy in an International Context.* NCES 2008-016. Washington, D.C.: Institute of Education Sciences, National Center for Education Statistics, U.S. Department of Education, 2007.

Balka, Don S., Ted H. Hull, Ruth Harbin Miles. *A Guide to Mathematics Leadership: Sequencing Instructional Change.* Thousand Oaks, Calif.: Corwin Press, 2009.

Baroody, Arthur J. "Learning: A Framework." In *Achieving Fluency: Special Education and Mathematics,* edited by Francis (Skip) Fennell, pp. 15–53. Reston, Va.: National Council of Teachers of Mathematics, 2011.

Baroody, Arthur J., Yingying Feil, and Amanda R. Johnson. "An Alternative Reconceptualization of Procedural and Conceptual Knowledge." *Journal for Research in Mathematics Education* 38 (March 2007): 115–31.

Battista, Michael T. "The Influence of Technology on Mathematics Learning in Elementary and Middle School Classrooms." In *Teaching and Learning Mathematics: Translating Research for Elementary School Teachers,* edited by Diana V. Lambdin and Frank K. Lester, pp. 55–60. Reston, Va.: National Council of Teachers of Mathematics, 2010.

Bay-Williams, Jennifer M., and Socorro Herrera. "Is 'Just Good Teaching' Enough to Support the Learning of English Language Learners? Insights from Sociocultural Learning Theory." In *The Learning of Mathematics,* Sixty-ninth Yearbook of the National Council of Teachers of Mathematics (NCTM), edited by W. Gary Martin and Marilyn E. Strutchens, pp. 43–63. Reston, Va.: NCTM, 2007.

Bay-Williams, Jennifer, and Karen Karp, eds. *Growing Professionally: Readings from NCTM Publications for Grades K–8.* Reston, Va.: National Council of Teachers of Mathematics, 2008.

Bennett, Albert, Eugene Maier, and Ted Nelson. *Math and the Mind's Eye.* Portland, Ore.: The Math Learning Center, 1988–98.

Black, Paul, and Dylan Wiliam. "Assessment and Classroom Learning." *Assessment in Education* 5, no. 1 (1998): 7–74.

Boaler, Jo. *What's Math Got to Do with It: Helping Children Learn to Love Their Most Hated Subject—and Why It's Important for America.* New York: Viking, 2008.

Boaler, Jo, Dylan Wiliam, and Margaret Brown. "Students' Experiences of Ability Grouping—Disaffection, Polarisation, and the Construction of Failure." *British Educational Research Journal* 26 (December 2000): 631–48.

Brahier, Daniel J., ed. *Motivation and Disposition: Pathways to Learning Mathematics.* Seventy-third Yearbook of the National Council of Teachers of Mathematics (NCTM). Reston, Va.: NCTM, 2011.

Burris, Carol Corbett, Jay P. Heubert, and Henry M. Levin. "Accelerating Mathematics Achievement Using Heterogeneous Grouping." *American Educational Research Journal* 43, no. 1 (2006): 105–136.

Campbell, Patricia F. *Project IMPACT: Increasing Mathematics Power for All Children and Teachers.* Phase 1, Final Report. College Park, Md.: Center for Mathematics Education, University of Maryland, 1995.

———. "Elementary Mathematics Specialists: A Merger of Policy, Practice, and Research." In *Disrupting Tradition: Research and Practice Pathways in Mathematics Education,* edited by William F. Tate, Karen D. King, and Celia Rousseau Anderson, pp. 93–103. Reston, Va.: National Council of Teachers of Mathematics, 2011.

Campbell, Patricia F., and Nathaniel N. Malkus. "The Impact of Elementary Mathematics Coaches on Student Achievement." *The Elementary School Journal* 111 (March 2011): 430–54.

Chappell, Michaele F., Jeffrey Choppin, and Jenny Salls, eds. *Empowering the Beginning Teacher of Mathematics in High School.* Reston, Va.: National Council of Teachers of Mathematics, 2004.

Chappell, Michaele F., and Tina Pateracki, eds. *Empowering the Beginning Teacher of Mathematics in Middle School.* Reston, Va.: National Council of Teachers of Mathematics, 2004.

Chappell, Michaele F., Jane Schielack, and Sharon Zagorski, eds. *Empowering the Beginning Teacher of Mathematics in Elementary School.* Reston, Va.: National Council of Teachers of Mathematics, 2004.

Charles, Randy I., and Frank K. Lester, eds. *Teaching and Learning Mathematics: Translating Research for School Administrators.* Reston, Va.: National Council of Teachers of Mathematics, 2010.

Choy, Susan P. *Access and Persistence: Findings from 10 Years of Longitudinal Research on Students.* Washington, D.C.: American Council on Education, Center for Policy Analysis, 2002.

Civil, Marta. "Mathematics Education, Language Policy, and English Language Learners." In *Disrupting Tradition: Research and Practice Pathways in Mathematics Education,* edited by William F. Tate, Karen D. King, and Celia Rousseau Anderson, pp. 77–91. Reston, Va.: National Council of Teachers of Mathematics, 2011.

Clarke, Ben, Keith Smolkowski, Scott K. Baker, Hank Fien, Christian T. Doabler, and David J. Chard. "The Impact of a Comprehensive Tier 1 Core Kindergarten Program on the Achievement of Students at Risk in Mathematics." *The Elementary School Journal* 111 (June 2011): 561–84.

Coggins, Debra. "Strategies for Enhancing English Language Learners' Success with Mathematics." In *Leadership to Math Success for All,* NCSM Monograph 5, edited by Edna F. Bazik, pp. 22–30. National Council of Supervisors of Mathematics, 2007.

Committee on Science, Engineering, and Public Policy (CSEPP). *Rising Above the Gathering Storm: Energizing and Employing America for a Brighter Economic Future.* Washington, D.C.: National Academies Press, 2007.

Common Core State Standards Initiative (CCSSI). *Common Core State Standards for Mathematics. Common Core State Standards (College- and Career-Readiness Standards and K–12 Standards for English Language Arts and Math).* Washington, D.C.: National Governors Association Center for Best Practices and the Council of Chief State School Officers, 2010. http://www.corestandards.org.

Confrey, Jere, Alan P. Maloney, and Kenny H. Nguyen. *Learning Trajectories Display of the Common Core Standards for Mathematics.* New York: Wireless Generation, 2010.

Cooper, Harris. *Homework: What the Research Says.* Research Brief. Reston, Va.: National Council of Teachers of Mathematics, 2008.

Copley, Juanita V. *The Young Child and Mathematics.* 2nd ed. Washington, D.C.: National Association for the Education of Young Children; Reston, Va.: National Council of Teachers of Mathematics, 2010.

Corcoran, Sean P. *Can Teachers Be Evaluated by Their Students' Test Scores? Should They Be? The Use of Value-Added Measures of Teacher Effectiveness in Policy and Practice.* New York: Annenberg Institute for School Reform at Brown University, 2010.

Danielson, Charlotte. *Enhancing Professional Practice: A Framework for Teaching.* 2nd ed. Alexandria, Va.: Association for Supervision and Curriculum Development, 2007.

Darling-Hammond, Linda. "Securing the Right to Learn: Policy and Practice for Powerful Teaching and Learning." *Educational Researcher* 35 (October 2006), 13–24.

———. "The Flat Earth and Education: How America's Commitment to Equity Will Determine Our Future." *Educational Researcher* 36 (August/September 2007), 318–34.

———. *The Flat World and Education: How America's Commitment to Equity Will Determine Our Future.* New York: Teachers College Press, 2010.

Darling-Hammond, Linda, Ruth Chung Wei, Alethea Andree, Nikole Richardson, and Stelios Orphanos. *Professional Learning in the Learning Profession: A Status Report on Teacher Development in the United States and Abroad.* Palo Alto, Calif.: National Staff Development Council and the School Redesign Network at Stanford University, 2009.

Davies, Anne. "Involving Students in the Classroom Assessment Process." In *Ahead of the Curve: The Power of Assessment to Transform Teaching and Learning,* edited by Douglas Reeves, pp. 31–57. Bloomington, Ind.: Solution Tree, 2007.

Delcourt, Marcia A. B., Brenda H. Loyd, Dewey G. Cornell, and Marc D. Goldberg. *Evaluation of the Effects of Programming Arrangements on Student Learning Outcomes.* Charlottesville, Va.: University of Virginia, 1994.

Desimore, Laura M., Thomas Smith, David Baker, and Koji Ueno. "Assessing Barriers to the Reform of U.S. Mathematics Instruction from an International Perspective." *American Educational Research Journal* 42 (Fall 2005): 501–35.

Dick, Thomas P., and Karen F. Hollebrands. *Focus in High School Mathematics: Technology to Support Reasoning and Sense Making.* Reston, Va.: National Council of Teachers of Mathematics, 2011.

Doerr, Helen M., Lynn T. Goldsmith, and Catherine C. Lewis. *Mathematics Professional Development.* Research Brief. Reston, Va.: National Council of Teachers of Mathematics, 2010.

DuFour, Richard, Rebecca DuFour, Robert Eaker, and Gayle Karhanek. *Whatever It Takes: How Professional Learning Communities Respond When Kids Don't Learn.* Bloomington, Ind.: Solution Tree Press, 2004.

DuFour, Richard, Rebecca DuFour, Robert Eaker, and Thomas Many. *Learning by Doing: A Handbook for Professional Learning Communities at Work.* Bloomington, Ind.: Solution Tree Press, 2006.

Education Trust. *Gaining Traction, Gaining Ground: How Some High Schools Accelerate Learning for Struggling Students.* Washington, D.C.: Education Trust, 2005.

Elliott, Portia C., and Cynthia M. Elliott Garnett, eds. *Getting into the Mathematics Conversation.* Reston, Va.: National Council of Teachers of Mathematics, 2008.

Ellis, Mark W., and Carol E. Malloy, eds. *Mathematics for Every Student: Responding to Diversity, Grades 6–8.* Reston, Va.: National Council of Teachers of Mathematics, 2009.

Fennell, Francis (Skip), ed. *Achieving Fluency: Special Education and Mathematics.* Reston, Va.: National Council of Teachers of Mathematics, 2011.

Flores, Alfinio, and Carol E. Malloy, eds. *Mathematics for Every Student: Responding to Diversity, Grades 9–12.* Reston, Va.: National Council of Teachers of Mathematics, 2009.

Fosnot, Catherine Twomey, ed. *Models of Intervention in Mathematics: Reweaving the Tapestry.* Reston, Va.: National Council of Teachers of Mathematics; Upper Saddle River, N.J.: Pearson, 2010.

Fosnot, Catherine Twomey, and Bill Jacob. *Young Mathematicians at Work: Constructing Algebra.* Portsmouth, N.H.: Heinemann, 2010.

Fuson, Karen C. "Toward Computational Fluency in Multidigit Multiplication and Division." *Teaching Children Mathematics* 9 (February 2003): 300–305.

Fuson, Karen C., and Aki Murata. "Integrating NRC Principles and the NCTM Process Standards to Form a Class Learning Path Model That Individualizes within Whole-Class Activities." *NCSM Journal of Mathematics Education Leadership* 10 (Spring 2007): 72–91.

Gersten, Russell, Sybilla Beckmann, Benjamin Clarke, Anne Foegen, Laurel Marsh, Jon R. Star, and Bradley Witzel. *Assisting Students Struggling with Mathematics: Response to Intervention (RtI) for Elementary and Middle Schools.* NCEE 2009-4060. Washington, D.C.: National Center for Education Evaluation and Regional Assistance, Institute of Education Sciences, U.S. Department of Education, 2009a.

Gersten, Russell, David J. Chard, Madhavi Jayanthi, Scott K. Baker, Paul Morphy, and Jonathan Flojo. "Mathematics Instruction for Students with Learning Disabilities: A Meta-Analysis of Instructional Components." *Review of Educational Research* 79, no. 3 (2009b): 1202–42.

Gersten, Russell, and Benjamin S. Clarke. *Effective Strategies for Teaching Students with Difficulties in Mathematics.* Research Brief. Reston, Va.: National Council of Teachers of Mathematics, 2007.

Gersten, Russell, Nancy C. Jordan, and Jonathan R. Flojo. "Early Identification and Interventions for Students with Mathematics Difficulties." *Journal of Learning Disabilities* 38 (July/August 2005): 293–304.

Gonzales, Patrick, Trevor Williams, Leslie Jocelyn, Stephen Roey, David Kastberg, and Summer Brenwald. *Highlights from TIMSS 2007: Mathematics and Science Achievement of U.S. Fourth- and Eighth-Grade Students in an International Context.* NCES 2009-001 rev. Washington, D.C.: National Center for Education Statistics, Institute of Education Sciences, U.S. Department of Education, 2008.

Graham, Karen, Al Cuoco, and Gwen Zimmermann. *Focus in High School Mathematics: Reasoning and Sense Making in Algebra.* Reston, Va.: National Council of Teachers of Mathematics, 2010.

Griffin, Sharon A., Robbie Case, and Robert S. Siegler. "Rightstart: Providing the Central Conceptual Prerequisites for First Formal Learning of Arithmetic to Students at Risk for School Failure." In *Classroom Lessons: Integrating Cognitive Theory and Classroom Practice,* edited by Kate McGilly, pp. 25–49. Cambridge, Mass.: MIT Press, 1994.

Hanley, Tom V. "Commentary on Early Identification and Intervention for Students with Math Difficulties: Make Sense—Do the Math." *Journal for Learning Disabilities* 38 (July/August 2005): 346–49.

Heid, M. Kathleen, and Glendon W. Blume, eds. *Research on Technology and the Teaching and Learning of Mathematics.* Vol. 1, *Research Syntheses.* Charlotte, N.C.: Information Age; Reston, Va.: National Council of Teachers of Mathematics, 2008.

Hembree, Ray, and Donald J. Dessart. "Research on Calculators in Mathematics Education." In *Calculators in Mathematics Education,* 1992 Yearbook of the National Council of Teachers of Mathematics (NCTM), edited by James T. Fey, pp. 23–32. Reston, Va.: NCTM, 1992.

Herbel-Eisenmann, Beth, and Michelle Cirillo, eds. *Promoting Purposeful Discourse: Teacher Research in Mathematics Classrooms.* Reston, Va.: National Council of Teachers of Mathematics, 2009.

Hiebert, James. "Relationships between Research and the NCTM Standards." *Journal for Research in Mathematics Education* 30 (January 1999): 3–19.

Hiebert, James, and Douglas A. Grouws. *Effective Teaching for the Development of Skill and Conceptual Understanding of Number: What Is Most Effective?* Research Brief. Reston, Va.: National Council of Teachers of Mathematics, 2006.

———. "The Effects of Classroom Mathematics Teaching on Students' Learning." In *Second Handbook of Research on Mathematics Teaching and Learning,* edited by Frank K. Lester, pp. 371–404. Charlotte, N.C.: Information Age Publishing; Reston, Va.: National Council of Teachers of Mathematics, 2007.

Horn, Laura, and Anne-Marie Nuñez. *Mapping the Road to College: First-Generation Students' Math Track, Planning Strategies, and Context of Support.* Washington, D.C.: U.S. Department of Education, National Center for Education Statistics, 2000.

Hull, Ted H., Don S. Balka, and Ruth Harbin Miles. *A Guide to Mathematics Coaching: Processes for Increasing Student Achievement.* Thousand Oaks, Calif.: Corwin Press, 2009.

Jacobs, Jennifer K., James Hiebert, Karen Bogard Givvin, Hilary Hollingsworth, Helen Garnier, and Diana Wearne. "Does Eighth-Grade Mathematics Teaching in the United States Align with the NCTM Standards? Results from the TIMSS 1995 and 1999 Video Studies." *Journal for Research in Mathematics Education* 37 (January 2006): 5–32.

Kilpatrick, Jeremy, W. Gary Martin, and Deborah Schifter, eds. *A Research Companion to "Principles and Standards for School Mathematics."* Reston, Va.: National Council of Teachers of Mathematics, 2003.

Knapp, Michael S., Nancy E. Adelman, Camille Marder, Heather McCollum, Margaret C. Needels, Christine Padilla, Patrick M. Shields, Brenda J. Turnbull, and Andrew A. Zucker. *Teaching for Meaning in High-Poverty Schools.* New York: Teachers College Press, 1995.

Knight, Jim. *Instructional Coaching: A Partnership Approach to Improving Instruction.* Thousand Oaks, Calif.: Corwin Press, 2007.

Knight, Jim, ed. *Coaching: Approaches and Perspectives.* Thousand Oaks, Calif.: Corwin Press, 2009.

Lambdin, Diana V., and Frank K. Lester, eds. *Teaching and Learning Mathematics: Translating Research for Elementary School Teachers.* Reston, Va.: National Council of Teachers of Mathematics, 2010.

Larson, Matthew R. "A Curriculum Decision-Maker's Perspective on Conceptual and Analytical Frameworks for Studying Teachers' Use of Curriculum Materials." In *Mathematics Teachers at Work: Connecting Curriculum Materials and Classroom Instruction,* edited by Janine T. Remillard, Beth A. Herbel-Eisenmann, and Gwendolyn M. Lloyd, pp. 93–99. New York: Routledge, 2009.

Lester, Frank K., ed. *Second Handbook of Research on Mathematics Teaching and Learning.* Charlotte, N.C.: Information Age; Reston, Va.: National Council of Teachers of Mathematics, 2007.

Lobato, Joanne, and Frank K. Lester, eds. *Teaching and Learning Mathematics: Translating Research for Secondary School Teachers.* Reston, Va.: National Council of Teachers of Mathematics, 2010.

Loucks-Horsley, Susan, Katherine E. Stiles, Susan Mundry, Nancy Love, and Peter W. Hewson. *Designing Professional Development for Teachers of Science and Mathematics.* 3rd ed. Thousand Oaks, Calif.: Corwin Press, 2009.

Ma, Liping. *Knowing and Teaching Elementary Mathematics: Teachers' Understanding of Fundamental Mathematics in China and the United States.* Mahwah, N.J.: Lawrence Erlbaum, 1999.

Martin, W. Gary, Marilyn E. Strutchens, Stephen Stuckwisch, and Mohammed Qazi. "Transforming East Alabama Mathematics (TEAM-Math): Promoting Systemic Change in Schools and Universities." In *Disrupting Tradition: Research and Practice Pathways in Mathematics Education,* edited by William F. Tate, Karen D. King, and Celia Rousseau Anderson, pp. 105–18. Reston, Va.: National Council of Teachers of Mathematics, 2011.

Marzano, Robert J. *Classroom Assessment and Grading That Work.* Alexandria, Va.: Association for Supervision and Curriculum Development, 2006.

———. *The Art and Science of Teaching: A Comprehensive Framework for Effective Instruction.* Alexandria, Va.: Association for Supervision and Curriculum Development, 2007.

McCall, Martha S., Carl Hauser, John Cronin, G. Gage Kingsbury, and Ronald Houser. *Achievement Gaps: An Examination of Differences in Student Achievement and Growth.* Lake Oswego, Ore.: Northwest Evaluation Association, 2006.

McCrone, Sharon M., James King, Yuria Orihuela, and Eric Robinson. *Focus in High School Mathematics: Reasoning and Sense Making in Geometry.* Reston, Va.: National Council of Teachers of Mathematics, 2010.

McGatha, Maggie. *Mathematics Specialists and Mathematics Coaches: What Does the Research Say?* Research Brief. Reston, Va.: National Council of Teachers of Mathematics, 2009.

McKenzie Group. *Handheld Technology and Student Achievement: A Collection of Publications.* Houston, Tex.: McKenzie Group, 2001.

McKinsey & Company. *The Economic Impact of the Achievement Gap in America's Schools.* Washington, D.C.: McKinsey & Company, 2009.

McREL. *What We Know about Mathematics Teaching and Learning.* 3rd ed. Bloomington, Ind.: Solution Tree Press, 2010.

Middleton, James A., and Amanda Jansen. *Motivation Matters and Interest Counts: Fostering Engagement in Mathematics.* Reston, Va.: National Council of Teachers of Mathematics, 2011.

Mirra, Amy J. *Administrator's Guide: How to Support and Improve Mathematics Education in Your School.* Reston, Va.: National Council of Teachers of Mathematics; Alexandria, Va.: Association for Supervision and Curriculum Development, 2003.

Morris, Anne K., and James Hiebert. "Creating Shared Instructional Products: An Alternative Approach to Improving Teaching." *Educational Researcher* 40 (January/February 2011): 5–14.

Morris, Anne K., James Hiebert, and Sandy M. Spitzer. "Mathematical Knowledge for Teaching in Planning and Evaluating Instruction: What Can Preservice Teachers Learn?" *Journal for Research in Mathematics Education* 40 (November 2009): 491–529.

Moschkovich, Judit. "Bilingual Mathematics Learners: How Views of Language, Bilingual Learners, and Mathematics Communication Affect Instruction." In *Improving Access to Mathematics: Diversity and Equity in the Classroom,* edited by Na'ilah Suad Nasir and Paul Cobb, pp. 89–104. New York: Teachers College Press, 2007.

———. "Supporting Mathematical Reasoning and Sense Making for English Learners." In *Focus in High School Mathematics: Fostering Reasoning and Sense Making for All Students,* edited by Marilyn E. Strutchens and Judith Reed Quander, pp. 17–35. Reston, Va.: National Council of Teachers of Mathematics, 2011.

National Center for Education Statistics (NCES). *The Nation's Report Card: Mathematics 2009.* NCES 2010-451. Washington, D.C.: Institute of Education Sciences, U.S. Department of Education, 2009.

National Council of Supervisors of Mathematics. *The PRIME Leadership Framework: Principles and Indicators for Mathematics Education Leaders.* Bloomington, Ind.: Solution Tree Press, 2008.

National Council of Teachers of Mathematics (NCTM). *An Agenda for Action.* Reston, Va.: NCTM, 1980.

———. *Curriculum and Evaluation Standards for School Mathematics.* Reston, Va.: NCTM, 1989.

———. *Professional Standards for Teaching Mathematics.* Reston, Va.: NCTM, 1991.

———. *Principles and Standards for School Mathematics.* Reston, Va.: NCTM, 2000.

———. *Curriculum Focal Points for Prekindergarten through Grade 8 Mathematics: A Quest for Coherence.* Reston, Va.: NCTM, 2006.

———. *Mathematics Teaching Today: Improving Practice, Improving Student Learning.* 2nd ed. Updated, revised version, edited by Tami S. Martin, of *Professional Standards for Teaching Mathematics* (1991). Reston, Va.: NCTM, 2007.

———. *Focus in High School Mathematics: Reasoning and Sense Making.* Reston, Va.: NCTM, 2009.

———. *Making It Happen: A Guide to Interpreting and Implementing Common Core State Standards for Mathematics.* Reston, Va.: NCTM, 2010.

National Mathematics Advisory Panel (NMAP). *Foundations for Success: The Final Report of the National Mathematics Advisory Panel.* Washington, D.C.: U.S. Department of Education, 2008.

National Research Council (NRC). *Adding It Up: Helping Children Learn Mathematics.* Edited by Jeremy Kilpatrick, Jane Swafford, and Bradford Findell. Mathematics Learning Study Committee, Center for Education, Division of Behavioral and Social Sciences and Education. Washington, D.C.: National Academy Press, 2001.

———. *How Students Learn: Mathematics in the Classroom.* Committee on *How People Learn, A Targeted Report for Teachers.* M. Suzanne Donovan and John D. Bransford, eds. Division of Behavioral and Social Sciences and Education. Washington, D.C.: National Academies Press, 2005.

———. *Mathematics Learning in Early Childhood: Paths toward Excellence and Equity.* Committee on Early Childhood Mathematics. Christopher T. Cross, Taniesha A. Woods, and Heidi Schweingruber, eds. Center for Education, Division of Behavioral and Social Sciences and Education. Washington, D.C.: National Academies Press, 2009.

National Science Board. *Science and Engineering Indicators 2008.* 2 vols. Arlington, Va.: National Science Foundation, 2008.

No Child Left Behind Act of 2001, Public Law 107-110, 115 Statute 1425. 107th Cong., 1st sess. January 8, 2002.

Organisation for Economic Co-operation and Development (OECD). *PISA 2009 Results: What Students Know and Can Do—Student Performance in Reading, Mathematics, and Science.* Vol. 1. Paris: OECD, 2010. http://dx.doi.org/10.1787/9789264091450-en.

Pashler, Harold, Patrice M. Bain, Brian A. Bottge, Arthur Graesser, Kenneth Koedinger, Mark McDaniel, and Janet Metcalfe. *Organizing Instruction and Study to Improve Student Learning.* NCER 2007-2004. Washington, D.C.: National Center for Education Research, Institute of Education Sciences, U.S. Department of Education, 2007.

Perry, Rebecca, and Catherine Lewis. "Building Demand for Research through Lesson Study." In *Research and Practice in Education: Building Alliances, Bridging the Divide,* edited by Cynthia E. Coburn and Mary Kay Stein, pp. 131–45. Lanham, Md.: Rowan & Littlefield Publishing Group, 2010.

Popham, W. James. *Transformative Assessment.* Alexandria, Va.: Association for Supervision and Curriculum Development, 2008.

Rampey, Bobby D., Gloria S. Dion, and Patricia L. Donahue. *NAEP 2008 Trends in Academic Progress.* NCES 2009-479. Washington, D.C.: National Center for Education Statistics, Institute of Education Sciences, U.S. Department of Education, 2009.

Reed, Douglas S. "Is There an Expectations Gap? Educational Federalism and the Demographic Distribution of Proficiency Cut Scores." *American Educational Research Journal* 46, no. 3 (2009): 718–42.

Reed, Judith. *What Can We Learn from Research?* Research Brief. Reston, Va.: National Council of Teachers of Mathematics, 2008.

Reys, Barbara, and Francis (Skip) Fennell. "Who Should Lead Instruction at the Elementary School Level? A Case for Mathematics Specialists" *Teaching Children Mathematics* 9 (January 2003): 277–82.

Reys, Robert, Barbara Reys, Richard Lapan, Gregory Holliday, and Deanna Wasman. "Assessing the Impact of Standards-Based Middle Grades Mathematics Curriculum Materials on Student Achievement." *Journal for Research in Mathematics Education* 34 (January 2003): 74–95.

Roberts, Sally K. "Not All Manipulatives and Models are Created Equal." *Mathematics Teaching in the Middle School* 13 (August 2007): 6–9.

Rose, Heather, and Julian R. Betts. "The Effect of High School Courses on Earnings." *The Review of Economics and Statistics* 86, no. 2 (2004): 497–513.

Saul, Mark, Susan Assouline, and Linda Jensen Sheffield, eds. *The Peak in the Middle: Developing Mathematically Gifted Students in the Middle Grades.* Reston, Va.: National Council of Teachers of Mathematics, 2010.

Sawada, Daiyo, Michael Piburn, Kathleen Falconer, Jeff Turley, Russell Benford, Irene Bloom, and Eugene Judson. *Reformed Teaching Observation Protocol (RTOP).* ACEPT Technical Report No. IN00-1. Tempe, Ariz.: Arizona Collaborative for Excellence in the Preparation of Teachers, 2000.

Schmidt, William H., Leland S. Cogan, Richard T. Houang, and Curtis C. McKnight. "Content Coverage Differences across Districts/States: A Persisting Challenge for U.S. Education Policy." *American Journal of Education* 117, no. 3 (2011): 399–427.

Schmoker, Michael J. *Results Now: How We Can Achieve Unprecedented Improvement in Teaching and Learning.* Alexandria, Va.: Association for Supervision and Curriculum Development, 2006.

Schneider, Mark. *National Assessment of Educational Progress: Mapping 2005 State Proficiency Standards onto the NAEP Scales.* Washington, D.C.: Institute of Education Sciences, National Center for Education Statistics, 2007.

Schoenfeld, Alan H. "Making Mathematics Work for All Children: Issues of Standards, Testing, and Equity." *Educational Researcher* 31 (January/February 2002): 13–25.

Seeley, Cathy L. *Faster Isn't Smarter: Messages about Math, Teaching, and Learning in the 21st Century.* Sausalito, Calif.: Math Solutions, 2009.

Senk, Sharon L., and Denisse R. Thompson, eds. *Standards-Based School Mathematics Curricula: What Are They? What Do Students Learn?* Mahwah, N.J.: Lawrence Erlbaum, 2003.

Shaughnessy, J. Michael, Beth Chance, and Henry Kranendonk. *Focus in High School Mathematics: Reasoning and Sense Making in Statistics and Probability.* Reston, Va.: National Council of Teachers of Mathematics, 2009.

Shuhua, An. *The Middle Path in Math Instruction: Solutions for Improving Math Education.* Lanham, Md.: Scarecrow Education, 2004.

Silver, Edward. "Examining What Teachers Do When They Display Their Best Practice: Teaching Mathematics for Understanding." *Journal of Mathematics Education at Teachers College* 1, no. 1 (2010): 1–6.

Silver, Edward A., and Mary Kay Stein. "The QUASAR Project: The 'Revolution of the Possible' in Mathematics Instructional Reform in Urban Middle Schools." *Urban Education* 30 (January 1996): 476–521.

Slavin, Robert E., and Cynthia Lake. "Effective Programs in Elementary Mathematics: A Best-Evidence Synthesis." *Review of Educational Research* 78, no. 3 (2008): 427–515.

Small, Marion. *Good Questions: Great Ways to Differentiate Mathematics Instruction.* New York: Teachers College Press; Reston, Va.: National Council of Teachers of Mathematics, 2009.

Small, Marian, and Amy Lin. *More Good Questions: Great Ways to Differentiate Secondary Mathematics Instruction.* New York: Teachers College Press; Reston, Va.: National Council of Teachers of Mathematics, 2010.

Smith, Margaret S., and Mary Kay Stein. *5 Practices for Orchestrating Productive Mathematics Discussions.* Reston, Va.: National Council of Teachers of Mathematics, 2011.

Spillane, James P. "The Distributed Leadership Studies: A Case Study of Research in and for School Practice." In *Disrupting Tradition: Research and Practice Pathways in Mathematics Education,* edited by William F. Tate, Karen D. King, and Celia Rousseau Anderson, pp. 7–19. Reston, Va.: National Council of Teachers of Mathematics, 2011.

Stein, Mary Kay, and Julia H. Kaufman. "Selecting and Supporting the Use of Mathematics Curricula at Scale." *American Educational Research Journal* 47 (September 2010): 663–93.

Stein, Mary Kay, Jennifer Russell, and Margaret Schwan Smith. "The Role of Tools in Bridging Research and Practice in an Instructional Improvement Effort." In *Disrupting Tradition: Research and Practice Pathways in Mathematics Education,* edited by William F. Tate, Karen D. King, and Celia Rousseau Anderson, pp. 33–44. Reston, Va.: National Council of Teachers of Mathematics, 2011.

Stein, Mary Kay, and Margaret S. Smith. "The Influence of Curriculum on Students' Learning." In *Mathematics Curriculum: Issues, Trends, and Future Directions,* Seventy-second Yearbook of the National Council of Teachers of Mathematics (NCTM), edited by Barbara J. Reys and Robert E. Reys, pp. 351–62. Reston, Va.: NCTM, 2010.

Stiff, Lee V., Janet L. Johnson, and Patrick Akos. "Examining What We Know for Sure: Tracking in Middle Grades Mathematics." In *Disrupting Tradition: Research and Practice Pathways in Mathematics Education,* edited by William F. Tate, Karen D. King, and Celia Rousseau Anderson, pp. 63–75. Reston, Va.: National Council of Teachers of Mathematics, 2011.

Stigler, James W., and James Hiebert. *The Teaching Gap: Best Ideas from the World's Teachers for Improving Education in the Classroom.* New York: The Free Press, 1999.

Stigler, James W., and James Hiebert. "Improving Mathematics Teaching." *Educational Leadership* 61, no. 5 (2004): 12–16.

Stigler, James W., and Belinda J. Thompson. "Thoughts on Creating, Accumulating, and Utilizing Shareable Knowledge to Improve Teaching." *The Elementary School Journal* 109 (May 2009): 442–57.

Strutchens, Marilyn E., and Judith Reed Quander. *Focus in High School Mathematics: Fostering Reasoning and Sense Making for All Students.* Reston, Va.: National Council of Teachers of Mathematics, 2011.

Tate, William F., Karen D. King, and Celia Rousseau Anderson, eds. *Disrupting Tradition: Research and Practice in Mathematics Education.* Reston, Va.: National Council of Teachers of Mathematics, 2011.

Tate, William, and Celia Rousseau. "Access and Opportunity: The Political and Social Context of Mathematics Education." In *Handbook of International Research in Mathematics Education,* edited by Lyn D. English, pp. 271–99. Mahwah, N.J.: Lawrence Erlbaum, 2002.

Thompson, Patrick W. "On Professional Judgment and the National Mathematics Advisory Panel Report: Curricular Content." *Educational Researcher* 37, no. 9 (2008): 582–87.

Truxaw, Mary P., and Thomas C. DeFranco. "Mapping Mathematics Classroom Discourse and Its Implications for Models of Teaching." *Journal for Research in Mathematics Education* 39 (November 2008): 489–525.

Turner, Julianne C., Kristen Bogner Warzon, and Andrea Christensen. "Motivating Mathematics Learning: Changes in Teachers' Practices and Beliefs during a Nine-Month Collaboration." *American Educational Research Journal* 48 (June 2011): 718–62.

Usiskin, Zalman. "The Case of the University of Chicago School Mathematics Project—Secondary Component." In *Perspectives on the Design and Development of School Mathematics Curricula,* edited by Christian R. Hirsch, pp. 173–82. Reston, Va.: National Council of Teachers of Mathematics, 2007.

Wallace, Ann H., and Susan P. Gurganus. "Teaching for Mastery of Multiplication." *Teaching Children Mathematics* 12 (August 2005): 26–33.

White, Dorothy Y., Julie Sliva Spitzer, and Carol E. Malloy, eds. *Mathematics for Every Student: Responding to Diversity, Grades Pre-K–5.* Reston, Va.: National Council of Teachers of Mathematics, 2009.

Wiliam, Dylan. *Five "Key Strategies" for Effective Formative Assessment.* Research Brief. Reston, Va.: National Council of Teachers of Mathematics, 2007.

Wiliam, Dylan, and Marnie Thompson. "Integrating Assessment with Instruction: What Will It Take to Make It Work?" In *The Future of Assessment: Shaping Teaching and Learning,* edited by Carol Anne Dwyer, pp. 53–82. Mahwah, N.J.: Lawrence Erlbaum, 2007.

Williams, Belinda. "Reframing the Reform Agenda." In *Closing the Achievement Gap: A Vision for Changing Beliefs and Practices,* edited by Belinda Williams, pp. 178–96. Alexandria, Va.: Association for Supervision and Curriculum Development, 2003.

Witzel, Bradley S., Cecil D. Mercer, and M. David Miller. "Teaching Algebra to Students with Learning Difficulties: An Investigation of an Explicit Instruction Model." *Learning Disabilities Research and Practice* 18 (May 2003): 121–31.

Wixson, Karen. "A Systemic View of RTI Research." *The Elementary School Journal* 111 (June 2011): 503–10.

Zbiek, Rose Mary. "The Influence of Technology on Secondary School Students' Mathematics Learning." In *Teaching and Learning Mathematics: Translating Research for Secondary School Teachers,* edited by Joanne Lobato and Frank K. Lester, pp. 39–44. Reston, Va.: National Council of Teachers of Mathematics, 2010.

Zimmermann, Gwen, Patricia Guinee, Linda M. Fulmore, and Elizabeth Murray, eds. *Empowering the Mentor of the Beginning Mathematics Teacher.* Reston, Va.: National Council of Teachers of Mathematics, 2009.

———. *Empowering the Mentor of the Experienced Mathematics Teacher.* Reston, Va.: National Council of Teachers of Mathematics, 2009.

———. *Empowering the Mentor of the Preservice Mathematics Teacher.* Reston, Va.: National Council of Teachers of Mathematics, 2009.